Contents

Introduction		ii
Unit 1	Place-value, ordering, estimating, rounding	4
Unit 2	Understanding addition and subtraction	6
Unit 3	Money and 'real life' problems, mental calculation strategies	8
Unit 4	Measures	10
Unit 5	Shape and space, symmetry	12
Unit 6	Shape and space	14
Unit 7	Counting, properties of number and number sequences	16
Unit 8	Understanding multiplication and division	18
Unit 9	Money and 'real life' problems, making decisions and checking results	20
Unit 10	Fractions	22
Unit 11	Understanding addition and subtraction and time	24
Unit 12	Handling data	26
Unit 13	Place-value, ordering, estimating, rounding and reading scales	28
Unit 14	Understanding addition and subtraction, mental calculation strategies	30
Unit 15	Money and 'real life' problems, making decisions and checking results	32
Unit 16	Shape and space	34
Unit 17	Measures	36
Unit 18	Time	38
Unit 19	Counting, properties of number and number sequences	40
Unit 20	Understanding addition and subtraction	42
Unit 21	Understanding multiplication and division	44
Unit 22	Money and 'real life' problems	46
Unit 23	Fractions	48
Unit 24	Handling data	50
Unit 25	Place-value, ordering, estimating, rounding	52
Unit 26	Understanding addition and subtraction	54
Unit 27	Money and 'real life' problems, making decisions and checking results	56
Unit 28	Shape and space	58
Unit 29	Shape and space	60
Unit 30	Measures and time	62
Unit 31	Counting, properties of numbers, number sequences and reasoning about numbers	64
Unit 32	Understanding multiplication and division	66
Unit 33	Money and 'real life' problems	68
Unit 34	Fractions	70
Unit 35	Understanding addition and subtraction	72
Unit 36	Handling data	74
Termly Matching Charts		76
Recording Sheets		79

Introduction

 ## Problem solving

Following the introduction of the **National Numeracy Strategy** *Framework for Teaching Mathematics*, overall standards of numeracy in primary schools have been steadily rising. However, of the five strands covered by the Framework, there is one which teachers often find harder to integrate into their lessons – solving problems. The *Problem Solving* series of books is designed to help you meet the objectives of this solving problems strand. The books provide suggestions on how to incorporate opportunities for children to develop more sophisticated problem-solving strategies into your teaching.

Solving problems is at the heart of mathematical learning and should be integrated throughout the other strands where it can be placed in context. It is vital that children recognise that methods, as well as answers, are important. They should use their knowledge in other areas of mathematics to interpret problems and check that their methods and answers are reasonable. *Problem Solving* aims to encourage children to extend their individual thinking skills to make sense of problems and identify the operations needed to solve them. However, they will still need help to develop the skills needed to explain and demonstrate their methods, as well as to explore the reasons for any wrong answers.

Problem Solving, therefore, provides detailed notes for the teacher on how to model and present the problems and puzzles. The photocopiable pupil pages contain simple text, so difficulty with reading will not preclude participation in mathematical activities. The teacher's notes often give more background to the task, allowing you to give support to the children who need it.

 ## Planning and teaching

Each *Problem Solving* unit has been carefully matched to the **National Numeracy Strategy** *Sample Medium Term Plans*, so as to reduce the time needed for planning. Termly matching charts are provided to enable you to dovetail the relevant *Problem Solving* Unit into your planning, whatever materials you are using to deliver the Daily Maths Lesson. There are 36 units within each book, each providing five problems. These can be used flexibly as one activity per day, or presented altogether at the end of each week or topic.

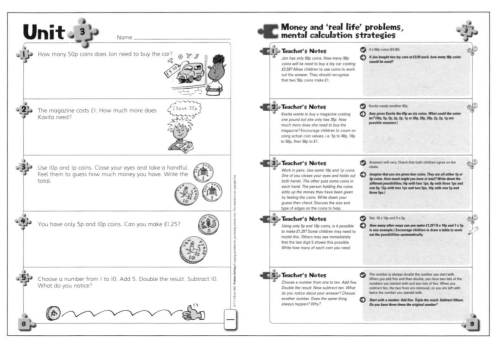

The notes on the right-hand page of each unit provide all the information you need to use the sheets. The 'Teacher's Notes' section explains the problem, tells you of any preparation or special equipment you will need, and suggests ways in which the problem can be presented to the children. Suggested words which you may wish to use have been italicised, but you can, of course, adapt these. Alongside the 'Teacher's Notes' you will also find the answers ✓ , and an activity which can be used as a follow up ➡ . These follow-up activities can be used in whole class teaching or as an extension for more able children. Some may also be used to form the basis of a homework investigation. There are also occasional tips 💡 . These range from alternative methods to support children who are struggling, to ways to present children's results.

Resources

Where resources other than the photocopiable recording sheet are required, these are mainly materials which are generally available in the classroom. The use of other equipment has been kept to a minimum. Any additional materials required are indicated by the following icons.

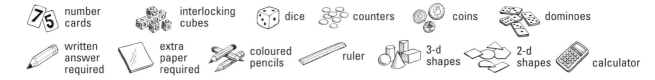

number cards · interlocking cubes · dice · counters · coins · dominoes · written answer required · extra paper required · coloured pencils · ruler · 3-d shapes · 2-d shapes · calculator

Differentiation

Open-ended problems are used wherever possible, enabling each child to work at his or her own level of attainment. Added flexibility is given by the format of the pupil page. Many of the problems can be answered orally. Where a written answer is required, or in cases where the pupil page provides additional essential information, the ✏ icon indicates this on the teacher's page. The activity suggested on the teacher's page can often be adapted to suit the needs of your class, or tailored for individual children.

Working together

Throughout the book children are encouraged to solve problems by working collaboratively. There is an emphasis on practical activities for the whole class and for work in groups and pairs. The children's learning is continually reinforced by activities such as explaining methods to a partner, or setting problems for their partner to solve. In this way, children are encouraged to go beyond completing the activity, and also to reflect on their methods.

Assessment

Space is provided on each pupil page ⊟ to record the children's achievement if you choose to allocate marks. You will need to decide upon your own marking scheme as totals for each unit will vary depending on how and whether you ask children to record their work for each problem.

Two recording sheets are provided at the back of this book:
• Individual record sheet
• Class record sheet.

The 'Individual record sheet' may be photocopied for each child. Space is provided for you to record comments on the child's achievement in each Unit. The 'Class record sheet' lists the Units and can be used to summarise the performance of the class as a whole. It is designed to provide an overall picture of the children's achievements, and help to identify any areas which may benefit from further reinforcement. These sheets can be used in your own record keeping, or passed to a receiving teacher at the end of the year.

Unit 1

Name _____

1 Write Ian's number.

one hundred, five tens and three ones

2 Write the next 5 numbers after Susie's number.

The number before my number is 99

3 Count back in tens between these numbers.

92   59

How many numbers do you say?

4 Each mark is a teacher. How many stickers?

	Hundreds	Tens	Ones
Total	IIII	IIII II	III

5 Put these numbers in order.

121   32   97   104   141   77

Write a number that can go in the middle.

Place-value, ordering, estimating, rounding

UNIT 1

  Teacher's Notes

 Ian's number is 153.

Ian is thinking of a number. It has one hundred, five tens and three ones. What is Ian's number? Write it in figures. Repeat, saying other numbers for the children to write down.

 Ask children to write down a 3-digit secret number and describe it to a partner in this way.

---

2 **Teacher's Notes**

 101, 102, 103, 104, 105.

Susie is thinking of a number. The number before it is ninety-nine. Write down the five numbers that come after Susie's number. Repeat, replacing Susie's number with another number. Ensure children understand that Susie's number is 100, so the first number they write is 101.

 Encourage children to play this game with their partner asking questions such as, *The number before my secret number is eighty-seven. Can you write down the number that is ten more?* Let children be creative as they make up similar puzzles of their own.

---

 3 **Teacher's Notes**

 3 numbers – 82, 72, 62.

Count back in tens from ninety-two. Don't count back past fifty-nine! How many numbers have you said? Repeat for other numbers.

 Count back from ninety-two in fives. How many numbers do you need to say to count back to exactly fifty-seven? (7 numbers)

---

4 **Teacher's Notes**

 473 stickers.

Look at your worksheets. If each tally mark represents a sticker, how many stickers are there altogether? Repeat, drawing different tallies on the board.

 If we added another hundred stickers how many more marks would we need? Which part of the table should the mark go in? How would we change the tally chart to show the new number?

---

 5 **Teacher's Notes**

 The numbers should be ordered 32, 77, 97, 104, 121, 141. Any number between 97 and 104 could be placed in the middle of the set of numbers. Discuss the ways in which children have ordered the numbers.

Write these numbers in order. Now write a number that would come in the middle of the set of numbers and become the fourth number in the sequence. Ask children to write other numbers to fit in different places in the sequence.

 How many different numbers could have been placed in this position? Write them down and share answers with your partner.

Unit 2

1 There are 18 sweets altogether. How many could each bag have?

2 How many points do Team B need to draw with Team A?

3 Here is a hundred domino: | 65 | 35 |

Make these into hundred dominoes.

| | 45 | | 75 | | | | 85 |

4 Here is an addition table. What number patterns can you see?

+	1	2	3	4	5
1	2	3	4	5	6
2	3	4	5	6	7
3	4	5	6	7	8
4	5	6	7	8	9

5 Make two additions using these numbers.

3   5   8

Now make two subtractions.

6

Understanding addition and subtraction

 Teacher's Notes

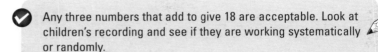

Here are three bags, each one containing some sweets. There are eighteen sweets altogether. How many sweets could be in each bag? Write down some suggestions. Allow children to use counters to model the possibilities if necessary.

✓ Any three numbers that add to give 18 are acceptable. Look at children's recording and see if they are working systematically or randomly.

➡ *If each bag contains one more sweet than the previous bag, can you calculate the number of sweets in each bag? (The first bag has five sweets, the second has six, and the third has seven.)*

 Teacher's Notes

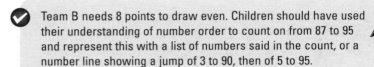

At the school sports day, Team A has ninety-five points and Team B has eighty-seven points. How many points does Team B need to score to draw even with Team A? Record some jottings to show how you calculated the answer.

✓ Team B needs 8 points to draw even. Children should have used their understanding of number order to count on from 87 to 95 and represent this with a list of numbers said in the count, or a number line showing a jump of 3 to 90, then of 5 to 95.

➡ *How many points does each team need to reach one hundred? (Team A needs 5 points, Team B needs 13 points.)*

 Teacher's Notes

Here is a 'hundred domino'. The two numbers on the domino add to make one hundred. These dominoes each have one number missing. Work out the number needed to make each domino a 'hundred domino'.

✓ The missing numbers are 55, 25 and 15.

➡ *If the dominoes were 'ninety dominoes' and the numbers added to make ninety, what would the missing numbers be? (45, 15, 5)*

 Teacher's Notes

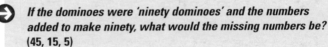

Look at your worksheets. Here is part of an addition table. Look for any number patterns you can see and take turns to describe them to your partner. Try an addition table using different numbers.

✓ There are many possible answers, for example: the numbers in columns run in order 2, 3, 4 . . .; the numbers in rows are in order 2, 3, 4 . . .; the numbers in the 'left to right' diagonals go up in twos; the numbers in the 'right to left' diagonal are all the same.

➡ *Outline a square of four numbers, e.g. 5, 6, 6, 7. Total the numbers in opposite corners of the square, e.g. 5 + 7 and 6 + 6. What do you notice? (Both pairs have the same total.) Does this happen with any square of four numbers? Investigate to find out.*

 Teacher's Notes

Use the numbers three, five and eight to create two addition sentences and two subtraction sentences. Look at the number sentences you have made and explain the patterns to your partner. What do you notice about the addition and the subtraction sentences?

 3 + 5 = 8, 5 + 3 = 8, 8 − 3 = 5, 8 − 5 = 3. Children should explain the inverse relationship between addition and subtraction. They may notice that the number 8 appears as the 'answer' in the addition sentences and as the 'first number' in the subtraction sentences.

 Investigate these two statements to discover if they are true or not. a) Numbers can be added in any order and the same total is always reached. b) Numbers can be subtracted in any order and the number left is always the same. (The first statement is true, the second is untrue.)

Unit 3

Name _____

1 How many 50p coins does Jon need to buy the car?

2 The magazine costs £1. How much more does Kavita need?

3 Use 10p and 1p coins. Close your eyes and take a handful. Feel them to guess how much money you have. Write the total.

4 You have only 5p and 10p coins. Can you make £1.25?

5 Choose a number from 1 to 10. Add 5. Double the result. Subtract 10. What do you notice?

8

Money and 'real life' problems, mental calculation strategies

UNIT
3

❶ Teacher's Notes

Jon has only 50p coins. How many 50p coins will he need to buy a toy car costing £3.59? Allow children to use coins to work out the answer. They should recognise that two 50p coins make £1.

✅ 8 x 50p coins (£4.00).

➡️ *If Jon bought two toy cars at £3.59 each, how many 50p coins would he need?*

❷ Teacher's Notes

Kavita wants to buy a magazine costing one pound but she only has 35p. How much more does she need to buy the magazine? Encourage children to count on using actual coin values, i.e. 5p to 40p, 10p to 50p, then 50p to £1.

✅ Kavita needs another 65p.

➡️ *Amy gives Kavita the 65p as six coins. What could the coins be?* (50p, 5p, 5p, 2p, 2p, 1p or 20p, 20p, 20p, 2p, 2p, 1p are possible answers.)

❸ Teacher's Notes

Work in pairs. Use some 10p and 1p coins. One of you closes your eyes and holds out both hands. The other puts some coins in each hand. The person holding the coins adds up the money they have been given by feeling the coins. Write down your guess then check. Discuss the size and type of edges on the coins to help.

✅ Answers will vary. Check that both children agree on the totals.

➡️ *Imagine that you are given four coins. They are all either 1p or 5p coins. How much might you have in total? Write down the different possibilities.* (4p with four 1ps, 8p with three 1ps and one 5p, 12p with two 1ps and two 5ps, 16p with one 1p and three 5ps.)

❹ Teacher's Notes

Using only 5p and 10p coins, is it possible to make £1.25? Some children may need to model this. Others may see immediately that the last digit 5 shows this is possible. Write how many of each coin you need.

✅ Yes. One way is 10 x 10p and 5 x 5p.

➡️ *How many other ways can you make £1.25?* (9 x 10p and 7 x 5p is one example.) Encourage children to draw a table to work out the possibilities systematically.

❺ Teacher's Notes

Choose a number from one to ten. Add five. Double the result. Now subtract ten. What do you notice about your answer? Choose another number. Does the same thing always happen? Why?

✅ The number is always double the number you start with. When you add five and then double, you have two lots of the numbers you started with and two lots of five. When you subtract ten, the two fives are removed, so you are left with twice the number you started with.

➡️ *Start with a number. Add five. Triple the result. Subtract fifteen. Do you have three times the original number?*

Unit 4

Name _____

1 Sunita and Jamie walk to school.
Circle who takes longer.

2 If these strips of card were joined together,
how long would the new strip be?

← 32 cm →

← 26 cm →

3 How long will it take to bake
15 cakes?

The cakes take 30 minutes to cook.

We can fit three in the oven at once.

4 Draw a picture of a tree near your school.

Guess the distance round the trunk.

5 Each brick weighs 2kg. What is the weight
of all the bricks?

10

 **Measures**

Teacher's Notes

Jamie walks eight hundred and thirty metres to school. Sunita walks at the same speed but has to walk nine hundred metres to school. Who do you think takes longer? Write your answer, and then explain your reasoning to a partner.

 Sunita takes longer, as she has further to go.

In pairs, ask children to walk the same distance. Who gets there first? Talk about why the same distance was covered in different times? Discuss factors that affect this, such as speed, obstacles, etc. *What would happen if Sunita jogged to school? Would it still take her longer than Jamie to get there?*

 Teacher's Notes

Two strips of cardboard are twenty-six centimetres and thirty-two centimetres long. If I place them end to end, what will the total length be? Allow children to use 30 cm rulers to help them. The first strip is 2 cm longer than one ruler and the second is 4 cm shorter, so the total length will be 2 cm shorter than two rulers together.

 32 cm + 26 cm = 58 cm.

 I cut a third length of cardboard so that the total length is eighty centimetres. How long is the third piece of cardboard? Draw a picture to help you imagine the problem and decide on the maths needed to solve it. **(22 cm)**

Teacher's Notes

Dan and Melissa are busy baking cakes for the school fair. They can fit three cakes in the oven at one time. The cakes take thirty minutes to cook. How long will it take them to bake fifteen cakes?

 Two and a half hours (five lots of 30 minutes).

 Use your answer to help you work out how long it would take to bake thirty cakes. How did you work out the answer? Try to explain in writing or with a calculation.

Teacher's Notes

Estimate the distance round the girth of a tree in the school grounds. Plan how you could measure this distance. What equipment would you use? Where would you measure? If you were comparing measurements between different trees, what things do you need to do to make it fair? Talk these things through with a partner.

 This depends on the tree chosen and whether the children actually carry out the measurements at all. The main focus for discussion should be methodology, e.g. should we use a tape measure, string or a ruler? Should we measure round the widest part of the tree or at a set height from the ground?

 Repeat the task trying out different approaches to solve the problem. *If you wanted to cut a slice through the trunk of the tree, what shape would you see?* **(A circular shape)**

Teacher's Notes

Look at the section of brick wall on your worksheets. A truck delivered the bricks needed to build the wall. How heavy were all the bricks? Each brick weighed two kilograms. With this piece of information, how can you calculate the total weight of the bricks in the wall?

 64 kg. Encourage children to use the layout of the bricks in the wall to calculate the total number of bricks, rather than counting them individually, i.e. 4 rows with 8 bricks in each = 4 x 8 = 32. Then that number should be multiplied by the weight of one brick, i.e. doubled.

 How many bricks would be needed to make a wall twice as high? What would the bricks weigh?

Unit 5

Name _____

1   Complete this picture. Reflect the shape across the line of symmetry.

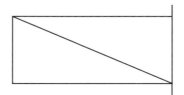

2   Draw some shapes with one line of symmetry.

3   Test these shapes. How many lines of symmetry do they have?

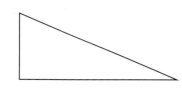 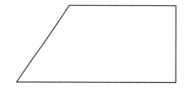 

4   Draw some triangles with one line of symmetry.

5   Find some objects that have line symmetry. Make a list of them.

Shape and space, symmetry

1 Teacher's Notes

Complete this picture. The vertical line is a line of symmetry. Reflect the shape across the line of symmetry. Children may need to copy the shape onto squared paper to help them draw the reflection accurately. Encourage them to draw the rectangle image first, then the diagonal.

✓

→ ***Can you complete this picture in the same way?***

2 Teacher's Notes

Draw a capital A on the board and show its vertical line of symmetry. This shape has only one line of symmetry. Can you draw other shapes with only one line of symmetry?

✓ There are many possible answers, for example: isosceles triangle, T-shape.

→ ***Draw a shape that has more than one line of symmetry. Can you find items in the classroom which have more than one line of symmetry?***

3 Teacher's Notes

Look at the shapes on your worksheet. Find a way to test each shape to see how many lines of symmetry each shape has.

✓ None of the shapes have lines of symmetry – children may have cut them out and folded them in different ways to check this, or used a mirror.

→ ***Is it possible to draw a five-sided shape with no lines of symmetry? Try to draw one on dotty paper. (Many are possible, e.g.***

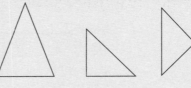

)

4 Teacher's Notes

Children will need spotted or squared paper and scissors. How many different triangles can you draw which have only one line of symmetry? When you have drawn them on dotty or squared paper, cut them out and fold them to check the line of symmetry.

✓ Many answers are possible. Here are some examples:

→ ***Is it possible to draw a square which has only one line of symmetry? Explain your answer.***

5 Teacher's Notes

Find some objects in the classroom which have line symmetry. Make a list of them. Encourage the children to look for regular shapes that they know are symmetrical, e.g. rectangular doors or tabletops. Write how many lines of symmetry each has.

✓ There are lots of possible items.

→ ***Sort this list according to the number of lines of symmetry each object has.***

Unit 6

Name _____

1 Draw the rest of this square.

2 Draw a triangle that has a right angle.

3 Can you draw a triangle with a right angle and all three sides the same length?

4 Draw this shape after a half turn.

5 Colour each section either red or blue. How many different squares can you make?

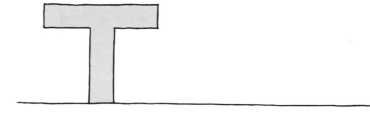

Shape and space

1 Teacher's Notes

On your worksheets, there is one side of a secret square. Can you complete the rest of the square? What if it was one side of a triangle? Would all your triangles be the same?

✓ The completed square should have four 2 cm sides.

➔ ***Can you draw a square that is twice the size? How would you go about this? What measurements would you need to take? Discuss your ideas with a partner then have a go.*** Check children draw a 4 cm x 4 cm square.

2 Teacher's Notes

Draw a triangle that has a right angle. You may like to discuss the properties of a triangle, e.g. number of sides and corners. Model right angles by asking children to look at squares and rectangles, e.g. their worksheets.

✓ There are many different right-angled triangles. Here is one example:

➔ ***Draw a triangle that doesn't have a right angle. Which kind of triangles are easier to draw?***

3 Teacher's Notes

Try to answer this puzzle: Is it possible to draw a triangle with one right angle and three sides that are equal in length? How could you try to solve this problem? Allow children to use squared paper to ensure accurate right angles.

✓ It is not possible to draw a triangle with these properties. Children may have drawn a selection of triangles in an attempt to solve the problem.

➔ ***Write another puzzle and ask your partner to try to solve it.***

4 Teacher's Notes

Look at your worksheets. Here is a shape standing on a table. What would it look like after a half turn? Describe it to your partner. Now try and draw the shape in its new position.

✓

➔ ***Here is a hoop balancing on a table. If the hoop was moved through half a turn, where would its new position be? Does the hoop look any different in its new position? Why is this?***

5 Teacher's Notes

On your worksheet is a square divided into four. Use red and blue crayons or pencils to shade the square. Each quarter must be one solid colour. Compare with a partner. Have you created two different squares? Use squared paper to see how many different squares you can make by colouring in this way.

✓ There are four squares with one red and three blue in different position; four squares with one blue and three red; four squares with two blue and two red.

➔ ***We are going to change the rules. If one square could be identical to another when rotated, then it doesn't count. How many different squares are there now?***

Unit 7

Name _____

1

Yes

5, 50,
60, 45, 20,

No

4, 17,
23, 92

Write five numbers for the monster to eat.

2

Eleanor doubled these numbers.
What do you notice about the answers?

12   **13**   **21**   **19**

3

Look at the beads. Can you see the patterns?

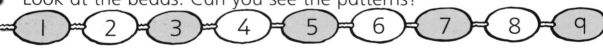

What colour is bead 27?
What colour is bead 34?
What colour is bead 50?

4

One of Gregory's secret numbers is odd. The other is even.
Is the total odd or even?

5

Can you find a times table with only odd answers?

that's odd!

16

Counting, properties of numbers and number sequences

1 Teacher's Notes

Alistair has a number monster that only eats certain numbers. On your worksheet are some numbers it will eat and some that it will not eat. Work out which types of numbers the monster eats and write down five new numbers for it to eat. Encourage children to see that the 'yes' numbers all end in 0 or 5.

 All the numbers given should be multiples of 5.

 Challenge children to make up an activity like this to swap with a partner.

2 Teacher's Notes

Eleanor doubled each of the numbers on the sheet. What do you notice about all the answers? Why do you think this has happened?

 They are all even.

 Now choose other whole numbers and double them. Do you ever get an odd number? (No.) Why do you think this is?

 Allow children to use counters or cubes to model doubling. Each counter or cube must have a pair when doubled, so there can never be an odd answer.

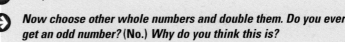

3 Teacher's Notes

The beads on this string are all black or white. Bead one is black, two is white and so on. What colour is bead twenty-seven? Bead thirty-four? Bead fifty? Can you work out a quick way of finding the answer rather than listing all the numbers?

 27 is black, 34 is white, 50 is white. Odd numbered beads are black, even numbered beads are white.

 What colour would bead 1000 be? (White because it is even.)

4 Teacher's Notes

Gregory has two secret numbers. One of the numbers is odd and one is even. He adds the two numbers. Which of the following is true? He gets an even number. He gets an odd number. You cannot tell unless you know the secret numbers.

 He gets an odd number.

 Can you explain why the result will always be odd? Use cubes to model how all the numbers bar one will be part of a pair, by making towers.

5 Teacher's Notes

The two times table has only even numbers two, four, six, eight and so on. Is there a times table that has only odd numbers? Why do you think this is?

 None of the times tables have only odd numbers. Every time a number is multiplied by an even number, the answer is even, so every times table will have some even answers.

Do you think there will be any odd answers in the 24 times table? The 17 times table?

Unit 8

Name _____

1 Can a number be a multiple of 4 and a multiple of 5? Explain your answer.

2 2 x 5 = 10. Use this to work out 2 x 6.

3 Start with 3. Double it, and keep doubling.
Will you ever get an answer of 100?

4 Helen multiplies her secret number by 10. She gets 110.
What is Helen's secret number?

5 Each shelf has the same number of CDs.
Draw different ways to put 24 CDs.

18

© T C O'Brien 2002. **Problem Solving 3** Copying permitted for purchasing schools only. This material is not copyright free.

Understanding multiplication and division

 ## Teacher's Notes

Is it possible for a number to be a multiple of four and also a multiple of five? Explain your answer. If children are unsure encourage them to write the first ten multiples of 4 in order, then the multiples of 5 until they find a number that appears in both lists.

✓ Yes. 20 is a multiple of both 4 and 5 because 4 x 5 = 20 and 5 x 4 = 20.

➔ **List all the numbers from one to fifty that are multiples of four and of five. Repeat for other pairs of numbers, e.g. 3 and 5, 4 and 10.**

 ## Teacher's Notes

If you know that two times five is ten, how can you work out two times six?

✓ 2 x 6 is one 2 more than 2 x 5, i.e. 10 + 2 = 12.

➔ **If you know what two times six is, how can you work out two times seven?**

 ## Teacher's Notes

If you start with three and you double and double and keep doubling, will you ever get an answer of one hundred? Encourage children to recognise that all answers must be multiples of 3. 100 is not a multiple of 3.

✓ No, you will not get 100.

➔ **How close can you get to 100?** (96)

 ## Teacher's Notes

Helen has a secret number. She multiplies it by ten and gets one hundred and ten. What is her secret number? Use place-value cards to model what happens to numbers when multiplied or divided by 10.

✓ Helen's secret number is 11.

➔ **What is the answer if Helen gets 1000?** (100)

20/7

 ## Teacher's Notes

The shopkeeper has to arrange CDs on shelves so that there are the same number on each shelf. He has 24 CDs to arrange. Show different ways to do this. How many shelves does he need? Allow children to use counters to help model the problem.

✓ 1 x 24, 2 x 12, 3 x 8, 4 x 6, 6 x 4, 8 x 3, 12 x 2, 24 x 1.

➔ **Without drawing it, think of an arrangement that has 5 shelves with 5 CDs on each shelf. How many CDs are there?**

 Represent the possible arrays on squared paper. This will help children to recognise multiplications quickly.

Unit 9

Name _____

1 How many 10p coins make £1.50?

2 You buy two yo-yos. How much change is there from £1?

yo-yos 40p

3 William has 10p. He has more than 2 coins.
What coins could he have?

4 Put these prices in order.

42p   £0.49   £0.02   £1.02   88p

5 Can you buy all these with a £5 note?

£1.15   £2.15   £0.35

20

Money and 'real life' problems, making decisions and checking results

---

1 — Teacher's Notes

How many 10p coins would make £1.50? Encourage children to try to work out the answer before counting coins to check. Can the children use the answer to find how many 5p coins make £1.50?

  15 coins.

 If you have twelve 10p coins and three 1p coins, how much money would you have? Try to write your answer in pence only and then in pounds and pence.

 Match up two 5p coins to one 10p to show how doubling can be used to find that twice as many 5p coins as 10p coins will be needed to make any particular amount.

---

2 — Teacher's Notes

You buy two yo-yos costing 40p each. How much change would you get if you gave the shopkeeper £1? If necessary, remind children that £1 = 100p.

 20p.

 Pose similar questions with different amounts of money.

---

3 — Teacher's Notes

William has more than two coins and they total 10p. Which coins could he have? Ask children to explain how they know they have found all the answers, e.g. drawing a table or writing a list.

  William could have: 1 x 5p, 2 x 2p, 1 x 1p; 1 x 5p, 5 x 1p; 5 x 2p; 4 x 2p, 2 x 1p; 3 x 2p, 4 x 1p; 2 x 2p, 6 x 1p; 1 x 2p, 8 x 1p.

Ask children to repeat the exercise with 20p.

---

4 — Teacher's Notes

Put the prices on your worksheets in order, explaining the order that you have chosen. Ask the children to explain how they have compared the prices. They should consider all amounts in the same unit, i.e. pounds or pence.

 Check the order is smallest to largest, e.g. £0.02, 42p, £0.49, 88p, £1.02, or visa versa.

How many pence are in each amount?

---

5 — Teacher's Notes

Would a £5 note be enough to pay for the items on your worksheets? Encourage children to add the pounds first and estimate the answer.

 Yes. The first two items total £3.30. The cost of the milk is 35p, so the total cost is £3.65. Ask the children to explain the different mental strategies they have used to add the three numbers together, including partitioning into pounds and pence.

After paying for the items, what change will you have from £5.00?

Unit

Name _____

1 Shade $\frac{1}{4}$ of this shape in two different ways.

2 Which is bigger $\frac{1}{3}$ or $\frac{1}{4}$? Draw some pictures to explain your answer.

3 Draw a circle around $\frac{1}{4}$ of these sweets.

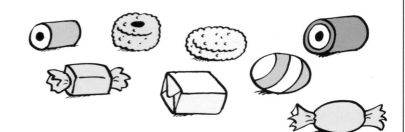

How many ways can you do this?

4 Put these fractions in order. Which is largest?

$$\frac{1}{2} \qquad \frac{1}{5} \qquad \frac{1}{4} \qquad \frac{1}{10}$$

5 Use cubes to build a tower.

Make $\frac{1}{2}$ of the cubes red.

Make $\frac{1}{4}$ of the cubes yellow.

The rest of the cubes are blue.

© T C O'Brien 2002. *Problem Solving 3*. Copying permitted for purchasing schools only. This material is not copyright free.

 **Fractions**

1. Teacher's Notes

Shade one quarter of this shape in two different ways.

✔ There are several possible answers. Here are two:

➡ Draw some divisions which don't split the shape into quarters. *How do we know which are quarters? (They are all the same size.)*

2. Teacher's Notes

Which is bigger, one third or one quarter? Draw some diagrams to help you to explain your reasoning. Remind children to think about how many equal pieces they need to cut, e.g. a pizza, into for each fraction.

✔ $\frac{1}{3}$ is bigger than $\frac{1}{4}$. Children may imagine an object being cut into pieces. They would get a bigger piece if it was shared between three than if it was shared between four.

➡ *Which is bigger, one third or one half? Use what you have discovered earlier to help you.*

3. Teacher's Notes

Here are eight sweets. Draw a ring around a quarter of them. How many different ways do you think this could be done? Encourage the children to explain that they need to ring two sweets, as the eight will be split into four equal-sized groups.

✔ Accept all the possible ways they have come up with, although it is unlikely that they will come up with all the possible ways – there are 28 (7 + 6 + 5 + 4 + 3 + 2 + 1) different ways in total.

➡ *If $\frac{1}{4}$ have been ringed, what fraction are left unringed? How many sweets is this?*

4. Teacher's Notes

Put the fractions on your worksheets in order to find out which is the largest. Explain your reasons for ordering them in that way.

✔ From smallest to largest the order is $\frac{1}{10}$ $\frac{1}{5}$ $\frac{1}{4}$ $\frac{1}{2}$. $\frac{1}{2}$ is the largest.

➡ *Think of a fraction that could be placed between $\frac{1}{5}$ and $\frac{1}{10}$.*

5. Teacher's Notes

Make a tower of cubes so that these fraction statements are true:
• $\frac{1}{2}$ *of the cubes are red*
• $\frac{1}{4}$ *of the cubes are yellow*
• *the rest of the cubes are blue.*

✔ Various answers are possible. Check that the relative fractions are true. One answer might be 8 red, 4 yellow, 4 blue. Notice that there will always be the same number of blue and yellow cubes.

➡ *If six cubes are blue, how many red and how many yellow are there? Build the tower that matches this description. (6 blue, 6 yellow, 12 red = 24 cubes in total.)*

Unit 11

Name _____

1 The video shop is shut from January 1st until January 15th. How many weeks is it shut?

2 There are 60 minutes in 1 hour. How many minutes in 4 hours?

3 Tell a story for 30 – 9.

4 Which three numbers between 1 and 8 add to give 16? Is there more than one way?

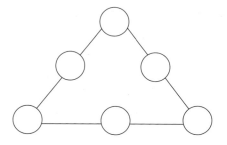

5 Arrange the numbers 1 to 6 in the circles. Each side of the triangle totals 9.

24

Understanding addition and subtraction and time

 ## Teacher's Notes

The video shop is shut from January 1st until January 15th while the owners are on holiday. How many weeks is the shop shut for? Explain the stages you went through to calculate the answer.

 14 days, which is the same as two weeks because there are seven days in one week.

 Can you calculate how many weeks there are until your birthday? You might want to calculate the months first this time.

Teacher's Notes

There are sixty minutes in one hour. Can you calculate how many minutes there are in four hours? Encourage children to explain their answer, e.g. using doubling, adding four lots of 60.

 4 x 60 minutes = 240 minutes.

 You are at school from 9am until 3pm, which is six hours. How many minutes are you at school for?

Teacher's Notes

Tell a real life story for thirty take away nine. Ensure that the children's stories are appropriate for the subtraction operation. Can they tell the story in a different way to make an addition story?

 There are many possible stories, for example, 'I had 30p and spent 9p'.

 Ask the children for a completely different story based on the same numbers.

Teacher's Notes

Which three numbers between one and eight add to give sixteen? Is there more than one way to do this? How many different ways are there? Discuss systematic ways to check that all the answers have been found, e.g. drawing a table.

 There are five ways: 1 + 7 + 8; 2 + 6 + 8; 3 + 5 + 8; 3 + 6 + 7 and 4 + 5 + 7.

 If the total was eighteen, would there be greater or fewer ways to do this? Explore to find out.

Teacher's Notes

Can you arrange the numbers one to six in the circles so that each side of the triangle adds to give nine? Ask the children to think about why 4, 5 and 6 cannot be on the same side or appear at a vertex.

 Check that the sides add to give 9. The triangle should look as shown, or be a rotation or reflection of this layout.

 Is it possible to make each side total 10? What about 11?

Unit 12

1 What could this graph describe? Label the graph.

Ainsley	xxxxx	
Jack	x	
Alice	xx	
Reens		xxxx
Felicity		

2 Use numbers 1 to 20. Sort them into different groups.

3 Look at a TV guide. Find programmes that are on more than once a week.

4 Look at this pictogram. What does it tell you?

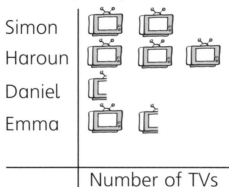

Simon

Haroun

Daniel

Emma

Number of TVs

= 2 TVs in the house

5 Pete thinks most children in year 3 go to bed before 8pm. Is this true for your class?

© T C O'Brien 2002. *Problem Solving 3.* Copying permitted for purchasing schools only. This material is not copyright free.

Handling data

1 Teacher's Notes

On your worksheets there is a simple graph. What could it describe? Discuss with the children the fact that all graphs need labels and titles so that we can understand them.

✓ There are many possible answers. For example, number of children in one's family, or number of pieces of pizza eaten.

➡ *Ask five friends how many people are in their family. Draw a graph to show what you find out.*

2 Teacher's Notes

Sort this set of numbers (1 to 20) into different groups. You can choose how to sort them but you need to be able to explain the sort afterwards. Try to draw a chart or diagram to show your sort. Allow children to use number cards to help them.

✓ Children may sort according to factors, odd/even, digits in unit/tens column . . . Make sure they have time to explain their sort and look at other children's sorting criteria too.

➡ *Sort this set of numbers (10 to 30) in a different way.*

3 Teacher's Notes

Use a TV programme guide for one week. Which programmes appear more than once in a week? How could you find out? How can you represent your findings?

✓ Regular programmes will vary, but will usually include programmes such as the news, serials or soaps.

➡ *Choose one of these programmes and create a chart to show the frequency of this programme during one week.*

4 Teacher's Notes

This is a pictogram showing how many TVs children have in their homes. One TV picture on the graph represents two TVs in the home. Which child has the most TVs? Where do you think they might be in the home? Compare the child with the fewest TVs and the one with the most – write a sentence that describes your findings. Think of a different way to present the same information – share your ideas with a partner.

✓ Haroun has the most (6). They might be in three bedrooms, lounge, kitchen, office . . . . Children may have suggested presenting the information in bar charts, lists or block graphs.

➡ *Try different ways of presenting this information. Which is the most effective?*

5 Teacher's Notes

Here is a statement: Most children in Year 3 classes go to bed before 8pm. How could you find out whether this statement is true or not? What information would you gather? How would you gather it? How would you present your findings?

✓ Children should have the opportunity to discuss strategies.

➡ *Go ahead and carry out your investigation.*

💡 You may need to discuss the meaning of 'most' with the children. Agree that it means more than half the class. *How many people is half the class?*

Unit 13

Name _____

1 Alicia wrote the numbers from 1 to 25.
How many times did she write '3'?
How many times did she write '4'?

2 What numbers do the arrows point to?

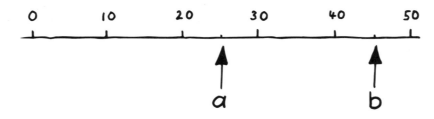

3 Use the digits 3, 4 and 5.
How many 3-digit numbers can you make?

4 Look at the number line. Write all the pairs of next-door numbers on it.

26   32

5 Round these numbers to the nearest hundred.

378   486   349

214   150

Place-value, ordering, estimating, rounding and reading scales

 Teacher's Notes

Alicia wrote the numbers from one to twenty-five. How many times did she write the digit three? How many times did she write the digit four? Encourage the children to try to work out the answer mentally first, before writing the numbers.

 Three times each (3, 13, 23) (4, 14, 24). *Can you see a link between your two answers?*

 ***How far would you need to go to have written the digit 3 and the digit 4 four times?* (Digit 3 from 1–30, digit 4 from 1–34.)**

---

2 Teacher's Notes

Ask the children to look at the number line on their sheets or draw it on the board. *What numbers do the arrows point to?* Draw similar number lines on the board and ask children to identify missing numbers.

 a) 25 and b) 45.

 Can you describe to a partner what you had to do before you worked out the numbers that were pointed to? What is the interval between two of the divisions/markers?

---

 3 Teacher's Notes

How many different 3-digit numbers can you make using the digits three, four and five? Try to work systematically by starting with the largest possible number. Allow children to use number cards to help them is necessary.

 543, 534, 453, 435, 354, 345

Choose other sets of three numbers, e.g. 7, 3, 8, and let the children re-organise them in the same way by changing the place-value of the digits. They should investigate to find out whether three numbers can always be re-organised to produce six different 3-digit numbers.

---

4 Teacher's Notes

Here are two numbers in place on a number line. Imagine all the numbers that come between these two numbers. Can you write down all the pairs of consecutive numbers (those that are next to each other) there are?

 26 and 27, 27 and 28, 28 and 29, 29 and 30, 30 and 31, 31 and 32.

 Think of another two numbers which have four pairs of consecutive numbers lying between them on the number line.

---

5 Teacher's Notes

Round these 3-digit numbers to the nearest hundred. Explain the decisions you have made in writing. You may need to remind children that 'half-way' numbers, i.e. those ending in 5, 50, 500, etc, always round up.

 378 → 400, 486 → 500, 349 → 300, 214 → 200, 150 → 200.

 Write down six numbers that could be rounded to one thousand.

Unit  14

Name _____

1 Complete these additions.

3 + 48 =   16 + 8 + 4 =

15 + 15 =   25 + 7 =

20 + 80 =

2 Complete these subtractions. What do you notice?

55 – 6 =   35 – 6 =

45 – 6 =   25 – 6 =

3 Make as many number sentences as you can with these numbers.

17   5   22

4 How many dominoes have 8 spots? Draw them.

5 The ✶ shows a missing digit. Write what number ✶ could be.

$$2✶ + ✶3 = 37 \qquad 66 – ✶4 = 2✶$$

$$✶5 – 2✶ = 12$$

Understanding addition and subtraction, mental calculation strategies

Teacher's Notes

Find ways to complete these additions. Explain the mental strategy you have used each time in words or with jottings.

✓ Children may have used different strategies but still got the right answer. Allow them to discuss alternatives, though these are the ones we would expect the children to use:
a) 51, start on 48 and count on 3. b) 30, double 15.
c) 100, using 2 + 8 = 10 to help. d) 28, add 16 + 4 first to make 20 then add 8. e) 32, partition 7 into 5 + 2, add 25 + 5 then 2.

➡ *Write a calculation that could be solved by adding a near multiple of ten then adjusting. (e.g. 35 + 28 = 35 + 30 − 2)*

Teacher's Notes

Complete these subtractions. Look at your complete number sentences. What do you notice? Can you describe the pattern and explain why it has been created?

✓ 55 − 6 = 49. 45 − 6 = 39. 35 − 6 = 29. 25 − 6 = 19.
Each start number has a 5 in the units column and requires a subtraction of 6 units. We subtract 5 first which leaves us with the multiple of 10 answer, then subtract 1 more. Each time the answer is 1 less than the multiple of 10, i.e. 50 − 1 = 49. Children will have different ways of explaining this, and number lines provide a useful way of helping them to find ways to explain their thinking.

➡ *Look at similar patterns and practice explaining how and why they have arisen. (e.g. 18 + 3, 28 + 3, 38 + 3, 48 + 3)*

Teacher's Notes

Here are three related numbers. Use these numbers to create as many complete number sentences, with answers, as you can.

✓ 17 + 5 = 22, 5 + 17 = 22, 22 − 17 = 5, 22 − 5 = 17.

➡ *Write a list of three related numbers and give them to your partner. They can work out the number sentences. Are there always four possible number sentences? Can you think of a set of three numbers which would give more or fewer than four number sentences? (If one number was repeated there would be less, e.g. 4 + 4 = 8.)*

Teacher's Notes

How many different ways can you choose two dominoes with a total of eight spots? Encourage children to recognise that e.g. 2 + 6 is the same domino as 6 + 2.

✓ There are three ways: 6 + 2, 5 + 3, 4 + 4.

➡ *Are there more ways to make other totals? Investigate.*

Teacher's Notes

Look at your worksheets. The star represents a missing digit. What could the star be in these number sentences?

✓ 24 + 13 = 37. 35 − 23 = 12. 66 − 44 = 22.

➡ *Make up some number puzzles like this for your partner to solve.*

💡 You may need to explain to children that they should think carefully about the positioning of the star, otherwise it will be impossible to solve the puzzle, e.g. 4* − 2* = 21. This has seven possible pairs of answers.

Unit 15

Name _____

1 Delroy has only 20p coins.
How many does he need to buy a football?

Footballs £1·59

2 What is the quickest way to work out how many 2p coins make 90p?

3 How much does it cost the Smith family to go swimming?

Grandad (age 67)
Mum (age 32)
Dad (age 38)
John (age 8)
Amy (age 1)

SWIMMING
Adult £1·20p
Senior citizen 50p
Child 60p
Under 2s Free

4 Harry buys a game for 74p. He pays for it exactly using 5 coins. Which coins does he use?

GAME

5 Amanda bought 3 items with a £1 coin.
She got 25p change.
What did she buy?

32p
acme ruler co.

25p

15 p

35 p

18 p

Money and 'real life' problems, making decisions and checking results

1 Teacher's Notes

Delroy has only 20p coins. How many coins should he give for a football costing £1.59? Encourage children to try to work out the answer mentally before using coins to help them.

✓ Delroy should give 8 coins.

→ *Harriet has 5 coins, all smaller than £1. Could she have exactly 90p? (Yes)*

2 Teacher's Notes

You need to find out how many 2p coins would make 90p. What is the most efficient way to work this out? Can you think of and describe a quicker way rather than counting in steps of 2p from zero all the way to 90p?

✓ 45 x 2p coins. The children may refer to halving as an efficient way to work this out; knowing that 90p is made of 90 x 1p coins but that two 1p coins can be exchanged for one 2p coin, generating the answer of 45 coins. They may need help to articulate this.

→ *How many 2p coins would make £9? (450)*

3 Teacher's Notes

On your worksheets are the prices it costs to swim at the local swimming baths. Work out the cost for this family to swim. Discuss the age a person must be to qualify for a senior citizen discount. Encourage children to try to work out the total cost mentally.

✓ 50p + £1.20 + £1.20 + 60p + 0p = £3.50.

→ *Make up a family whose total cost would be £3.40.*

4 Teacher's Notes

Harry chooses to buy a small game for 74p. He pays for it exactly using five coins. What could the five coins be? Is there only one possible answer? Investigate to find out.

✓ 50p + 10p + 10p + 2p + 2p.

→ *Think up another total that is made using five coins. Challenge your partner to work out what the coins are.*

5 Teacher's Notes

Amanda bought three items and received 25p change from her £1 coin. Which three items did she buy? Encourage children to see that they must first work out how much Amanda spent.

✓ There are two possible answers: ruler + pen + rubber or pen + pencil + pencil sharpener.

→ *Could Amanda have bought one of each item and still had some change from her £1 coin? Explain your answer.*

 Encourage children to use pairs to 10 to help them add up quickly.

Unit 16

1 This shape has one line of symmetry. Draw a 4-sided shape with no lines of symmetry.

2 Put two cubes on the table. How many faces can you see?

3 Clare folded a piece of paper and cut out a shape. Draw the piece of paper when she unfolds it.

4 Use these shapes to make a larger shape with one line of symmetry.

5 Here are two right-angled triangles. Use them to make some other shapes.

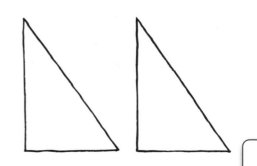

© T C O'Brien 2002. *Problem Solving 3* Copying permitted for purchasing schools only. This material is not copyright free.

Shape and space

1 Teacher's Notes

This shape has one line of symmetry. Can you draw a four-sided shape that has no lines of symmetry? Remind children how to check for symmetry, e.g. folding shapes, using mirrors, drawing on squared paper, etc.

 There are many possible answers, for example:

 Draw a four-sided shape that has two lines of symmetry. Compare your shape with your partner's. What other features do they have in common?

2 Teacher's Notes

If you hold a cube in your fingers and turn it around, you will see six square faces. If the cube is placed on a table, how many of its faces will you be able to see? Now imagine that two cubes are placed on a table. If you walk around the cubes and look at them without touching, how many faces will you see altogether?

 You will see 10 faces. (Two are hidden by the table.)

Ask children the same question with the cubes positioned like this.

3 Teacher's Notes

A piece of paper has been folded in half then a shape is drawn on, like this. Imagine that the shape is cut out of the paper and the paper is then unfolded. Draw what the shape will look like.

Encourage children to draw other shapes on folded paper and predict the outcomes.

4 Teacher's Notes

Here are three shapes. Can you fit them together to make a large shape with one line of symmetry? It may help to trace the shapes and cut them out so that you can move them around.

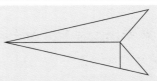

Can the same pieces be rearranged to create a different shape with one line of symmetry?

5 Teacher's Notes

Here are two identical right-angled triangles. How many different shapes can you make by placing these two triangles side by side? Can you name the shapes you have made? How many lines of symmetry does each shape have?

 It is possible to make six shapes: a rectangle, two isosceles triangles, two parallelograms and a kite.

Try this activity with other shapes.

Unit 17

Name _____

1 Hold a 1 kg weight. Write down three things you think will weigh 1 kg. Compare the weights. How close were you?

2 A medicine bottle holds 35 ml. How many 5 ml spoonfuls of liquid are in the bottle? Draw a picture to explain.

3 John is 136 cm tall. Amy is 25 cm taller. How tall is Amy? Show how you worked out your answer.

4 Which of these do you think is heaviest? How could you find out?

a litre of water   3 small balls

25 cubes   6 reading books

5 How many sheets of paper do you need to cover one wall of your classroom? How can you find out?

36

Measures

 Teacher's Notes

Hold a kilogram weight. Write down three items in the classroom that you think are about one kilogram in weight. Now compare the weights to see whether the objects you have chosen are about one kilogram in weight. Knowing this, how heavy might these items be?
a) chair b) table c) ten books d) an apple

✓ Children need to have a clear benchmark measure for 1 kg so that they can then use this to estimate weights more accurately. The actual weights of the objects will vary from class to class.

➔ ***What else might you weigh in kilograms?***

💡 Balance scales help children to visualise weight more easily than e.g. kitchen scales, since they are able to compare a 1 kg mass and other objects directly rather than just taking a reading.

 Teacher's Notes

A bottle of medicine holds thirty-five millilitres of liquid. How many five millilitre spoonfuls of liquid are in the bottle? Can you draw a picture to show how you 'see' the problem, then explain to a partner how you used maths to solve it.

✓ 7 spoonfuls. Drawings may show a large bottle with a scale on the side marked in 5 ml intervals, or seven spoons with 5 ml of liquid in each – whatever image children have, allow them time to explain it.

➔ **Ask children to make up another real life capacity problem and draw a picture to show a visual representation of it.**

 Teacher's Notes

John is one hundred and thirty-six centimetres tall. His older sister Amy is twenty-five centimetres taller. How tall is Amy? Use jottings to show how you calculated the answer.

✓ 136 cm + 25 cm = 161 cm. Children may have used partitioning, a blank number line, or counting on in steps of 10 and 1. Ask them to explain their method and then compare different children's methods. Which is the most efficient for these numbers?

➔ ***John's dad is 20 cm taller than Amy. He is twice as tall as John's younger brother Tom. How tall is Tom?***

 Teacher's Notes

Which do you think is heaviest: a litre of water, three small balls, twenty-five interlocking cubes, six reading books. Decide with a partner how you could compare the weights of the items to find out which item is the heaviest. Will your answers always be the same? Will the weights ever vary? How could you make it a fair test?

✓ The answers will depend on the objects chosen. Children should have realised that the weights may vary according to the size of the reading books and so on.

➔ ***Think of items whose weights never vary.***

💡 Scientifically, weight depends on gravitational pull exerted on an object. This can be measured using spring balances or a direct-reading scale. Mass – the quantity of matter an object contains – is found using balance scales. The distinction is rarely made in everyday usage though.

5 **Teacher's Notes**

How many sheets of A4 paper will it take to cover one wall of the classroom? Think about how you could solve this problem. What measurements would you take? How could you manage the task without having to actually cover the wall with paper? Would diagrams help?

✓ The answer depends on the size of the wall. Children should be measuring the size of the wall and the size of the paper and perhaps drawing a diagram to calculate how many pieces of paper would be needed.

➔ **If possible carry out the task so that children can see how close their answers are.**

Unit 18

Name _____

1 Write two activities that take you about 20 minutes.

2 The Ist of June was a Monday. On what day of the week was Michael born?

3 Andre is I year and 2 days younger than his brother. Andre's birthday is May Ist. When is his brother's birthday?

4 Ben's grandmother was born in 1940. How old is she now?

5 John got into the swimming pool at 2.30pm. He swam for 40 minutes. What time did he get out?

Time

1 Teacher's Notes

Name two activities that would take you about twenty minutes to do. Discuss the lengths of time some common activities take, e.g. drinking a glass of water, listening to one song on the radio, break time, etc. This will give children a benchmark to compare with.

✓ Many possible answers include eating a sandwich and walking to school etc, depending on personal circumstances.

→ ***What activity might take you about an hour to do?***

2 Teacher's Notes

Michael was born on June 12th. The first day of June was a Monday. On which day of the week was Michael born?

✓ Michael was born on a Friday.

→ ***Leah was born on May 29th in the same year. On which day of the week was Leah born?***

3 Teacher's Notes

Andre is one year and two days younger than his brother. If Andre's birthday is on May 1st, when is his brother's birthday? Repeat, giving the children some different dates for Andre's birthday.

✓ His brother would have a birthday on April 29th.

→ ***What day does your birthday fall on? Will it be the same next year? Look at a calendar to find out.***

4 Teacher's Notes

Ben's grandmother was born in 1940. How old is she now?

✓ The answer depends on the current year.

→ ***How many years is it until the year 2100? If people lived forever, how old would Ben's grandmother be then? Look at a calendar to find out.***

5 Teacher's Notes

John got into the swimming pool at 2.30pm and swam for forty minutes. What time did he get out?

✓ 3.10pm. Children may answer 2.70pm, forgetting that there are 60 minutes in each hour rather than 100.

→ ***Practice adding different amounts of minutes onto digital times so that children get used to bridging the hour.***

Unit 19

1 Can you crack the code?

HHTOOO = 213   HHHTTOOOO = 324
HHTTTTO =

2 Roll two 1 to 6 dice. Add the numbers together. Is the total odd or even? How many different totals can you make?

3 Janet has two numbers. Their sum is 5. Their product is 6. What are Janet's numbers?

4 What is the best way to count all the children in the school? Write down some ideas.

5 Start on 347 and count back in twos. Will you say 258? Why?

40

Counting, properties of numbers and number sequences

Teacher's Notes

Can you crack this code? If HHTOOO means two hundred and thirteen and HHHTTOOOO means three hundred and twenty-four, what is HHTTTTO?

 241.

 Use the code to write 335. (HHHTTTOOOOO). Write some numbers for your partner to solve. Who can decode 10 numbers quickest?

Teacher's Notes

Use two dice with numbers 1 to 6 on them. Roll the dice and add the 2 numbers shown to reach a total. Is the total odd or even? Continue with this recording the numbers rolled and the totals reached. Have the children rolled all the possible combinations? Are there more combinations that roll an odd total or an even total?

1 + 1 = 2 Even	1 + 2 = 3 Odd	1 + 3 = 4 Even
1 + 4 = 5 Odd	1 + 5 = 6 Even	1 + 6 = 7 Odd
2 + 2 = 4 Even	2 + 3 = 5 Odd	2 + 4 = 6 Even
2 + 5 = 7 Odd	2 + 6 = 8 Even	3 + 3 = 6 Even
3 + 4 = 7 Odd	3 + 5 = 8 Even	3 + 6 = 9 Odd
4 + 4 = 8 Even	4 + 5 = 9 Odd	4 + 6 = 10 Even
5 + 5 = 10 Even	5 + 6 = 11 Odd	6 + 6 = 12 Even

12 combinations that roll an even number, only 9 that roll an odd number.

 Now try with three dice – there are lots more combinations!

Teacher's Notes

Janet has two numbers. Their sum is 5 and their product is 6. What are the two numbers? Remind children that sum means added together and product means multiplied together.

 2 and 3.

 Choose two mystery numbers. Add them to find the sum, multiply them to find the product then give the clues to a partner and see if they can discover the mystery numbers.

Teacher's Notes

What would be the best way to count all the children in the school? Plan how you could tackle this huge problem in an efficient way. Write a list of what you would need to do.

 Discuss children's strategies and evaluate the effectiveness of them. Efficient techniques might be to get class lists from the secretary and add up all the class totals; another might be to go round and ask each teacher how many children are in their class, record the individual numbers then total. An inefficient strategy would be to line all the children up and count them one by one.

 Estimate how many children you think there may be in your school, then choose the most efficient strategy and complete the task.

Teacher's Notes

Start on three hundred and forty-seven and count back in twos. Will you say the number two hundred and fifty-eight? Explain your thinking.

 No. 347 is an odd number so a backwards count in twos would lead to all the odd numbers being said. 258 is an even number so it would not be said.

 What about if we count back in fives? Ensure that children realise that 258 will not be said because all the numbers will end in 7 or 2. Write some of the pattern to show this.

Unit 20

Name _____

1 Write some pairs of numbers that add up to 23.

2 Solve the number mystery using the clues.

The number has two digits.
It is an odd number.
It is greater than 50.
One of its digits is double the other digit.

3 Here is a number machine. What does it do?

17		29
4		16
35		47
23		35

4 Start at 0. Add three numbers to reach 500.

5 Use these numbers and signs. Make as many number sentences as you can.

17   32   15   34   49

+   −   =

© T C O'Brien 2002. *Problem Solving 3* Copying permitted for purchasing schools only. This material is not copyright free.

Understanding addition and subtraction

1 Teacher's Notes

Which two numbers could have a total of twenty-three? How many pairs can you find?

 There are many possible answers – e.g. 1 + 22, 2 + 21, 3 + 20, 4 + 19. Have the children worked systematically?

→ *If three numbers were added to give a total of twenty-three, would there be more combinations or fewer? Try to find out by systematically working out three numbers that add to give twenty-three.*

2 Teacher's Notes

Work out the mystery number from the following clues:
- *it has two digits*
- *it is odd*
- *it is greater than fifty*
- *one of its digits is double the other digit.*

 The mystery number is 63.

→ *Make up a mystery number puzzle like this for your partner to solve.*

 If children find this type of problem difficult, use a 1–100 number square to help. Cross off numbers as appropriate to match the clues.

3 Teacher's Notes

Here is a number machine. The numbers that go into the machine are all changed in the same way. What does the machine do to them? Encourage children to compare each pair of numbers, i.e. 17 and 29, 4 and 16, 35 and 47, 23 and 35 to look for a pattern.

 The machine is adding 12 to each number.

→ *Draw your own number machine, decide what it will do and show your partner some numbers going in and how they come out. Can they work out what your number machine does to numbers?*

4 Teacher's Notes

Start at zero and reach five hundred in three steps by adding amounts. How will you do it? Think up at least five different ways.

 Many possible answers, e.g. (+ 200, + 100, + 200), (+ 50, + 3, + 447). Make sure that children have used exactly three steps.

→ *Can you count back from ninety-seven to thirty-six in exactly three steps?*

5 Teacher's Notes

Use the numbers on your worksheet and the plus, subtract and equals signs to make as many different number sentences with answers, as you can.

 17 + 15 = 32, 15 + 17 = 32, 32 – 17 = 15, 32 – 15 = 17, 34 + 15 = 49, 15 + 34 = 49, 49 – 34 = 15, 49 – 15 = 34, 32 + 17 = 49, 17 + 32 = 49, 49 – 32 = 17, 49 – 17 = 32.

→ *Think of one more number that could be added to the list to create some new number sentences.*

Unit 21

1 Is Sam right?

All multiples of 4 are also multiples of 2

2 How many blocks of paint are on this tray?

3 Count in threes from 0. The pattern is odd, even, odd, even. Does this happen for other steps?

4 Lucy writes the multiples of 3 from 1 to 50.
Evan writes the multiples of 4 from 1 to 50.
Who writes more numbers? Why?

5 Paul needs three numbers to open the safe.
The numbers are all smaller than 50. They can be divided exactly by 5 and 3.
What are the numbers?

44

Understanding multiplication and division

Teacher's Notes

Sam says all multiples of four are also multiples of two. Is Sam correct? Explain your answer.

 Yes, Sam is right. 4 is a multiple of 2, so any multiple of 4 will also be a multiple of 2.

 Are all multiples of two also multiples of four? (No). Find a number which is divisible by two but not by four. (6, 10, 14,...)

Teacher's Notes

How many paint blocks are there in the tray? Can you find a quick way to work out the answer rather than counting each one? Is there a multiplication fact that would be useful?

 30 paint blocks. 5 x 6 = 30.

 Close your eyes and imagine a paint tray with four rows of six blocks. How many paint blocks are there? Draw a picture to show what you are imagining if this helps.

Use cubes or counters to represent the paint blocks and allow children to lay out the arrays themselves to help visualise the multiplications.

Teacher's Notes

When we count up in steps of three from zero the numbers we say are 'odd-even-odd-even' and so on. Does this happen when we count in other steps? Explore to find out.

 When we count up in any odd number step, the pattern odd-even-odd-even is reached. (fives = 5, 10, 15, 20, . . . sevens = 7, 14, 21, 28 . . . nines = 9, 18, 27, 36 . . .)

 If we count in steps of eleven, would the pattern odd-even-odd-even happen? Try it and see by adding eleven each time. Can you see any other patterns?

Teacher's Notes

Lucy writes the multiples of three from one to fifty. Evan writes the multiples of four from one to fifty. Who writes more numbers? Why is this? Encourage children to think whether they can answer the question without writing all the numbers.

 Lucy wrote more numbers. It took more steps for Lucy to reach 50 as she was counting on in a smaller step size.

 List the numbers that both children wrote.

Teacher's Notes

Paul is trying to open a secret safe. He must enter three special numbers. The numbers are smaller than fifty and can be divided exactly by five and by three. Which numbers are they?

 15, 30, 45.

 Can you list other numbers that are multiples of both five and three? Look at the numbers you have written. What else do they have in common?

Unit 22

Name _____

1 If you saved £2 each week, how much will you have after one year?

2 Which ice-creams have these children bought?

Small cone	70p
Medium cone	85p
Large cone	£1.10
Giant cone	£1.25
Ice lolly	60p
Wafer ice-cream	95p
Tub of ice-cream	55p

I bought 2 ice-creams. They cost £1.70

I bought 3 ice-creams. I spent £2.10

Amy   Paul

3 How many ways can you make 30p using silver coins?

o 30p

4 Who has more money?

I have 4 20ps 3 10ps, 3 2ps and 5 1ps

I have 1 50p, 2 20ps, 1 10p and 6 5ps

Sabrina   Tom

5 Taylor buys 3 lollies and 2 chocolate bars. How much change does he get from £1?

Lollies 14p   Choc 23p

Money and 'real life' problems

1 Teacher's Notes

If you saved £2 each week of the year, how much money would you have saved by the end of the year? Which facts do you need to use to help you work out the answer?

✔ £104. You need to know the number of weeks in the year (52) and be able to work out £2 x 52 using partitioning (50 + 50 + 2 + 2) or doubling (52 x 2).

➜ ***How many weeks would you need to save for to have £50?***

2 Teacher's Notes

Look at the price list of ice-creams on your worksheets. Which ice-creams have the children bought?
- *Amy bought 2 ice-creams and spent £1.70.*
- *Paul bought 3 ice-creams and spent £2.10.*

✔ Amy: ice lolly and large cone ; Paul: a tub, an ice lolly and a wafer.

➜ ***What would the total cost be to buy one of each type of ice-cream? Would £6 be enough to cover the cost?***

💡 Encourage children to see that in each case the children cannot have bought an odd number of items with a price ending in 5 or the totals spent would not be possible.

3 Teacher's Notes

Using silver coins only, how many different ways can you make 30p? Give the children other amounts to make using silver or bronze coins only. What amounts can't they make with silver coins?

✔ There are six ways:
20p + 10p
10p + 10p + 10p,
20p + 5p + 5p
10p + 10p + 5p + 5p
10p + 5p + 5p + 5p + 5p
5p + 5p + 5p + 5p + 5p + 5p.

➜ ***Which is the most efficient way? Explain your answer.***

4 Teacher's Notes

Which child has more money? Sabrina has four 20ps, three 10ps, three 2ps, and five 1ps. Tom has one 50p, two 20ps, one 10p, and six 5ps. Allow children to use coins to help them if necessary. Remind them to convert 100p to £1.

✔ Sabrina has £1.21, Tom has £1.30, so Tom has more money.

➜ ***Jessica has 35p more than Sabrina. How much does Jessica have?*** **(£1.56)**

5 Teacher's Notes

Taylor buys three lollies at 14p each and two chocolate bars at 23p each. How much change does he receive from £1?

✔ 22p change. He spends 42p + 46p = 88p. Allow children time to discuss the calculation strategies they have used and show the jottings that have accompanied these.

➜ ***Roll a dice twice to find out how many lollies and chocolate bars you will buy. Did you spend more than Taylor?***

Unit 23

Name _____

1. Write a fraction that is between $\frac{1}{2}$ and $\frac{1}{5}$.

2. Shade a $\frac{1}{3}$ of this shape in two different ways.

3. A farmer has 12 animals.
$\frac{1}{2}$ are cows, $\frac{1}{4}$ are sheep and the rest
are chickens. How many of each animal
does he have?

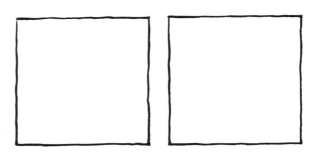

4. This rectangle has been divided into 4 parts. Is each
part a quarter?

5. When this jar is full it can hold 100 buttons.
How many do you think are in the jar now?

© T C O'Brien 2002. *Problem Solving 3.* Copying permitted for purchasing schools only. This material is not copyright free.

 **Fractions**

 Teacher's Notes

Write a fraction that is between one half and one fifth. You may need to discuss which fraction is the larger and why. Remind children to think of a pizza being cut into that number of pieces. They can then easily picture $\frac{1}{2}$ as larger than $\frac{1}{5}$.

 There are several possible answers, for example, one third.

 Write down two things that helped you to complete the task. Did you imagine pictures? Did you think about the numbers that make up the fraction? Share ideas with a partner, maybe they used different clues to help them.

Teacher's Notes

Shade one third of this shape in two different ways. Discuss that when the square is split into three pieces, they must be the same size (although not necessarily the same shape if the area is equal).

 There are many possible answers, including:

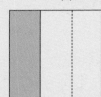 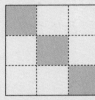

 Draw a round pizza. Divide it into three equal servings.

 Teacher's Notes

A farmer has 12 animals. Half are cows, one quarter are sheep and the rest are chickens. How many of each animal does he have? Encourage the children to see that they can work out how many cows and sheep there are in one step, but two steps are needed to find the number of chickens.

 He has 3 chickens, 3 sheep and 6 cows.

 He buys another seven sheep and one chicken from market. What fraction of his total animals are sheep now? (Half are sheep.)

Teacher's Notes

This rectangle has been divided into four parts. Explain to a partner whether you think each part of the rectangle is called a quarter or not.

 They are not quarters because although there are 4 parts, they are not equal in size. Children must be clear about this and be able to articulate it.

Suggest how the three vertical lines inside the rectangle could be moved so that the rectangle is divided into quarters.

 Teacher's Notes

When this jar is full it can hold one hundred buttons. About how many do you think are in the jar now? How many do you think have been used? Can you write fractions to show the amount used and the amount left?

 There are about 66 buttons in the jar. $\frac{1}{3}$ of the buttons have been used, $\frac{2}{3}$ are left.

 If another sixteen buttons are used, what fraction of buttons will be left?

 Encourage children to estimate using fractions and see that this is easier than guessing an exact number of buttons.

Unit 24

Name _____

1 Which pet is the most common?

How many children have dogs or cats?

Pet	Number of owners
Dog	12
Cat	6
Fish	18
Bird	4
Snake	3
Hamster	10

2 Use a train timetable. Find out how long it takes to go between two places.

3 Here is a graph. It shows the ages of the people in Tim's family. How old is each person?

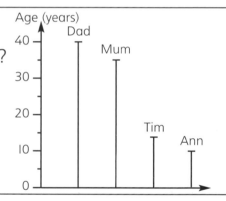

4 The numbers in the loop are winning numbers in a raffle. What do they have in common?

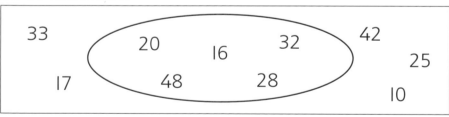

5 Look at the shapes in the Carroll diagram. Write the missing headings.

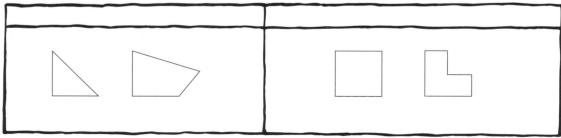

Handling data

Teacher's Notes

On your sheets is a frequency table showing pets that children have. Which pet is the most common? Why might this be? How many children have either dogs or cats? Some children have two different pets. Which combinations of pets do you think are most likely? Explain your answers.

✓ Fish are most common, perhaps because they are easy to keep. 18 children have either cats or dogs. Children may make suggestions as to likely combinations linked to how those animals get on together or how they are stored, e.g. not fish and cats.

→ ***Which is the most common pet in your class? Could you complete a frequency table to find out?***

2 Teacher's Notes

Use a train timetable to work out how long it would take to travel between two places. Does the journey time vary according to the time of day? Do some trains go faster than others? Gather data to help you answer those questions.

✓ This will depend on destinations chosen. Children should have noticed that some trains stop at more stations between the start and end of the journey and therefore take longer to cover the same distance.

→ ***Plan a trip involving two train journeys. Make sure you know what time you need to be at the station to come home.***

3 Teacher's Notes

On your worksheets is a graph of the ages of the people in Tim's family. How old is each person? Ask children to first work out how many years each division on the bar line graph represents, to help them read off the ages correctly.

✓ Dad is 40. Mum is 35. Tim is 15. Ann is 10.

→ ***Draw a similar graph for your family. You may have to use a slightly different scale to plot exact ages.***

4 Teacher's Notes

Look at the Venn diagram on your worksheets. It has been used to sort raffle tickets for the school summer fair. The winning numbers are inside the loop and the losing numbers are outside the loop. Look carefully at the numbers to see what makes a winning number. What do they have in common?

✓ Winning numbers are all multiples of 4.

→ ***What number closest to forty-seven would also be a winning number and would go inside the loop?***

5 Teacher's Notes

Look at the Carroll diagram on your worksheets showing some information about shapes. The shapes have been sorted into two columns according to their similarities and differences. Unfortunately the headings of the columns have been erased. Can you work out how they have been sorted?

✓ The heading on the first column should read 'shapes with one right angle', the heading on the second column should read 'shapes with more than one right angle'.

→ ***Draw two new shapes that could go into the Carroll diagram following your headings.***

Unit

1

Use the clues to find the number.

I am even.

I am smaller than 20.

I am a multiple of 7.

What number am I?

2

Use the digits 4, 2 and 7. Make the largest possible 3 digit number. Use each number once.

3

Look at the pattern in the first box. Make two more patterns in the other boxes.

1	6	7
2	5	8
3	4	9

4

Change each start number into the end number in one step.

Start	What to do	End
246		346
172		192
48		42
73		273
382		322

5

If this pattern carried on, what colour would bead 15 be?

Place-value, ordering, estimating, rounding

1 Teacher's Notes

Tell the children that they have to find a mystery number from some clues.
I am an even number.
I am less than twenty.
I am a multiple of seven.
What number am I?
Repeat for different mystery numbers.

 The secret number is 14.

→ *Take any one of the original sentences and delete it. What is the answer now?*

2 Teacher's Notes

What is the largest 3-digit number you can make using the digits 4, 2 and 7? Each digit can be used only once. Encourage the children to think logically about the relative size of the numbers when placed in the hundreds, tens or units positions.

✓ 742.

→ *What's the smallest 3-digit number you can make using the digits 4, 2 and 7? (247)*

3 Teacher's Notes

In the first box, the numbers one to nine are arranged in a pattern. Can you arrange the numbers one to nine to show two other number patterns?

✓ There are many possible answers, for example:

9	2	3
8	1	4
7	6	5

3	2	1
6	5	4
9	8	7

→ *Arrange the same digits one to nine into pairs totalling ten. Which number is left out? (1, 9, 2, 8, 3, 7, 4, 6, – number 5 is left out.)*

4 Teacher's Notes

Look at the table on your sheets. Can you change the start numbers into the end numbers in one step?

✓ + 100, + 20, 6, + 200, – 60.

→ *Change two hundred and seventy-nine to four hundred and sixty-three in three small steps. How could you do this in one large step? (small steps = + 200, – 10, – 6, one large step = + 184)*

5 Teacher's Notes

If this pattern continued, what colour would the fifteenth bead be? Encourage the children to recognise that they can count in twos, rather than drawing out all the beads.

 Grey.

→ *Can you use the number pattern of black and grey to work out what colour the thirty-fifth bead would be without counting up all the way to thirty-five? (Numbers ending in the digit 5 are alternately black then grey, e.g. 5 = black, 15 = grey, 25 = black, 35 = grey.)*

Unit  26

Name _____

1. John chooses 4 cars.
The numbers add
up to 20.
Circle his cars.

2. Gideon has 3 secret numbers. What are they?

$$A + B = 7 \qquad B + C = 8 \qquad A + C = 11$$

$$A = \qquad\qquad B = \qquad\qquad C =$$

3. Use 4 different odd numbers to make 20.
How many ways can you find?

4. I think of a number, and add 26. I get 47.
What was my starting number?

5. Look at the pairs of numbers. What do they have
in common?

76 $\longrightarrow$ 43

92 $\longrightarrow$ 59

78 $\longrightarrow$ 45

54

Understanding addition and subtraction

1 Teacher's Notes

John has eight toy racing cars. John chooses the four cars that he wants to use. The car numbers he has chosen add up to twenty. Which cars could he have chosen? Discuss the children's answers. Did they realise there were several possible answers?

✓ There are 7 different possibilities: 1, 4, 7, 8 or 2, 3, 7, 8 or 3, 4, 5, 8 or 1, 5, 6, 8, or 2, 4, 6, 8, or 3, 4, 6, 7 or 2, 5, 6, 7.

→ Tell the children that there are seven different ways. See if they can work out all the ways. *How many ways are there if the numbers add to twenty-two?*

2 Teacher's Notes

Gideon has three secret numbers. We'll call them A, B and C. A + B = 7, B + C = 8, A + C = 11. Can you work out what the numbers are? Encourage the children to discuss what the clues tell them. They should work out the possibilities for A and B, then see what C would be.

✓ A = 5, B = 2 and C = 6.

→ *Make a list of three secret numbers, invent some number clues and ask a partner to try and work out what the secret numbers are.*

3 Teacher's Notes

Using four odd numbers only, how many different ways can you make twenty? Ask the children what they will do first, e.g. list the odd numbers to 20. Encourage them to discuss strategies.

✓ There are different answers, e.g. 7 + 3 + 1 + 9 and 1 + 3 + 5 + 11.

→ *Is it possible to make twenty using three odd numbers?* (No, because odd + odd + odd would make an odd total and 20 is even.)

💡 Ask children questions to see whether they realise that making odd number bonds of 10 first is a helpful strategy.

4 Teacher's Notes

I think of a number and add twenty-six to it. The answer is forty-seven. What number did I start with? Check children understand that the calculation they need to perform is a subtraction.

✓ 21.

→ *Start at thirty-six, add forty, subtract eight. What is the answer?* (68) *Can you get from thirty-six to sixty-eight in one step only?*

5 Teacher's Notes

On your worksheets are some pairs of numbers. They have something in common to do with subtraction. Can you work out what it is? Children should find the difference between the units in each pair first, then look at the tens.

✓ They have a difference of 33.

→ *Colour pairs of numbers on a hundred grid that have a difference of thirty-three. Do you notice any patterns?*

Unit  27

Name _____

1 Can £1 be shared equally between 3 people?

2 You have £5. Which CDs can you buy?

£1.20   £2.70   £1.80   £1.60   £2.20   £1.40

3 It cost £10 for the Brown family to go to the zoo. Who could members of the Brown family be?

ZOO
Adult £3
Senior citizen £2
Child £1.50

4 The sweets have had $\frac{1}{4}$ of their prices taken off. What are the new prices?

12p   20p   8p   24p   16p
JELLY BEANS   FRUIT DROPS   MINTYS   CHOCOS   TOFFEES

5 Each child gives Gareth 20p sponsor money. How many children need to give 20p for Gareth to make £4?

Money and 'real life' problems, making decisions and checking results

1. Teacher's Notes

Can £1 be shared equally by three people? It may help children to imagine one hundred pence. Model sharing ten 1p coins between three children to show that 1p will be left over. Can they use this fact to answer the question?

 No. You have one penny left over.

 Can £10 be shared equally by three people?

2. Teacher's Notes

There's a sale at the CD shop. Some CDs are cheaper than others. You have chosen six CDs priced as follows: £2.70, £1.80, £1.40, £1.60, £2.20, £1.20. Unfortunately you only have £5 to spend today. How many CDs could you buy? Which ones could you choose? There may be different combinations that you could afford.

 There are lots of answers some of which equal £5 exactly, e.g. £1.60 + £2.20 + £1.20, some of which are less than £5, e.g. £1.20 + £1.60 + £1.40.

 The till in the shop is broken and they cannot give change. Which three CDs could you buy for exactly £5? Use your previous answers to help you.

3. Teacher's Notes

Look at the entry prices for the zoo. The Brown family spent £10 on entrance costs. Who could members of the Brown family be? You may need to explain that e.g. Grandma or Grandpa may not necessarily be senior citizens.

 Some examples include: two children + one adult + two senior citizens or two adults + two senior citizens or four children plus two senior citizens.

 How much would it cost for your family to go to the zoo?

4. Teacher's Notes

All items in the sweet shop are reduced in price. They have one quarter of the price taken off. What are the new prices? Children may need to use coins to share out into four groups to work out $\frac{1}{4}$ of each price.

 New prices 9p, 15p, 6p, 18p, 12p.

 A club football shirt used to cost £46. Now it costs £23. What fraction of the original price has been taken off?

5. Teacher's Notes

Gareth did a sponsored walk for charity. He is collecting sponsor money from his classmates. Each child gives him 20p. His target amount is £4. How many children must give money to Gareth for him to reach his target amount? Ask children to think about how many 20p coins make £1.

 20 children.

 He actually collects £6.20. How many children contributed? (31)

1 Draw a 4-sided shape with one right angle.

2 Name an object that is a sphere.

3 What is this 3-d shape?
It has 2 faces which are triangles.
It has 3 other faces which are rectangles.

4 Draw a shape that has 4 sides that are equal in length, but does not have 4 right angles.

5 This cube has diagonals on its faces. How many diagonals are there altogether?

Shape and space

Teacher's Notes

Draw a four-sided shape with only one right angle. Discuss common four-sided shapes, e.g. square, rectangle, parallelogram. *How many right angles do they have?*

 Here are some possible answers.

 Is it possible to draw a four-sided shape with exactly three right angles? (No)

2 Teacher's Notes

Name an object in real life that is a sphere. Encourage the children to name as many ball-shaped objects as possible.

 There are many possible answers, for example, a football, a globe, an orange.

 What is special about a sphere? Compare it to a cube. How is it different?

3 Teacher's Notes

I am imagining a 3-d shape. It has two faces that are triangles. They are both the same size. It has three other faces and these are rectangles. What shape am I thinking of? Ask children to a) find a 3-d shape that matches this description b) write down the name of the shape c) sketch the 3-d shape d) find a real life object that is this shape.

 Triangular prism, a 'Toblerone bar' is this shape.

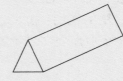

 Think of a 3-d shape and describe it to a partner in the same way. Can they work out what it is?

4 Teacher's Notes

A square has four sides that are equal in length and four right angles. Can you draw a shape that has four sides that are equal in length but does not have four right angles? The easiest way to draw this shape is to use squared paper. Draw the baseline, then offset the top line and join the ends of the lines.

Children will have drawn a rhombus. Children will not know the name of the shape, but it is useful for them to be familiar with it at this stage.

Can you draw a four-sided shape that has four right angles but that has every side a different length? (No, not possible)

5 Teacher's Notes

This cube has diagonals drawn on its faces. You can see six diagonals. How many are there altogether? Encourage children to think about how many faces a cube has, then multiply by 2 or double. Use actual cubes if children find it hard to imagine the non-visible faces.

There are 12 diagonals, two on each of six faces.

 How many diagonals are on the faces of this shape?

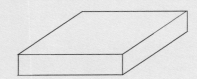

Unit 29

Name _____

1 Use four interlocking cubes. How many shapes can you make?

2 Draw round 2-d shapes with two lines of symmetry. What do they have in common?

3 Write the coordinates of each item on the map.

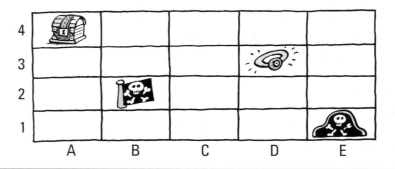

4 How many straws are there in this pattern? How many squares can you see?

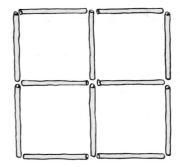

5 Draw six squares of the same size. Cut them out. Can you make them into a box with a lid?

Shape and space

1 Teacher's Notes

Take four interlocking cubes and fit them together in different ways to create new shapes. How many different shapes can you make? Draw some of them. Children may not realise that some shapes are duplicates, because they are rotations or reflections of other shapes.

✓ 8.

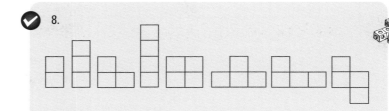

→ *With only three cubes, do you think you could make more shapes, fewer shapes, or the same amount as you did with four cubes?*

2 Teacher's Notes

Draw round a selection of 2-d shapes which have two lines of symmetry. Do they have any other features in common?

✓ Allow children time to explain the similarities they have noticed. Try to replace their everyday language with specific mathematical language where appropriate.

→ *Do all shapes with two lines of symmetry also contain at least one right-angled corner? Investigate this.*

3 Teacher's Notes

Here is a treasure map. Reading the letter coordinate first then the number coordinate, can you write a list to show where the treasure items can be found? Now draw one new item on your map without your partner seeing. They must ask you questions to try and find out where your new item is, e.g. Is it next to the gold ring? Is it below the treasure chest?

✓ D3 – gold ring; B2 – flag; E1 – pirate's hat; A4 – treasure chest.

→ *Which is the square to the right of the treasure chest? What is to the left of C2? Can you describe how to move from the treasure chest to the ring? What about from the hat to the flag?*

4 Teacher's Notes

Here are some straws arranged to make a pattern of squares. Look at the pattern carefully.
How many straws are there?
How many squares can you see?

✓ 12 straws; 5 squares – 4 small ones and one large one comprising the 4 small ones.

→ *How many more straws are needed to create another small square? Another large square?*

5 Teacher's Notes

Draw six identical squares and cut them out. Arrange them and tape them together so that they form a box with a lid. This is a net of a box. How many different ways can you arrange the squares so that they form a box?

✓ There are 12 different ways. For example:

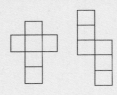

→ *Which of the nets are symmetrical?*

Unit 30

Name _____

1   Try to draw a line 15 cm long without a ruler.
Check it with a ruler.

2   Toby went into the shop at 10 past 9. He came out at
25 minutes to 10. How long was he in the shop?

3   How can you work out the
weight of 20 pairs of shoes?

4   An elephant drinks 35 litres of water a day. How
much water do 6 elephants need?

5   Estimate how long it takes to walk from your
classroom to the dining hall. How can you find out?

Measures and time

Teacher's Notes

Without using a ruler, draw a line which is about fifteen centimetres long. Then check the length of your line with a ruler. Ensure children are clear that they must align the zero on the scale with the beginning of the line.

 Children should measure their lines accurately to see how close they were.

 What is the length of your hand span in centimetres? Estimate first, and then measure.

 Encourage children to imagine items they know the length of to compare, e.g. an exercise book is about 20 cm long.

2 Teacher's Notes

Toby went into the shop at ten minutes past nine and came out at twenty-five minutes to ten. How long was he in the shop? If children are unclear, suggest they look at a clock to count round the minutes. Discuss different ways of describing times in words.

 25 minutes.

 ***Toby then went into the post office next door where he spent fifteen minutes and caught the bus home five minutes after that. What time was the bus?* (5 minutes to 10)**

3 Teacher's Notes

How much do you think 20 pairs of children's shoes weigh? Could you break the problem down into smaller stages to make it easier to solve? Would estimates help? I do not want twenty children to take off their shoes and weigh them!

 Suggestions may include weighing one pair of shoes and multiplying the amount by 20. Children should have discussions about the different sizes and weights of their shoes in deciding which pair to weigh.

 How many pairs of adult shoes would equal the weight of twenty pairs of children's shoes? Plan how we could find out.

4 Teacher's Notes

Each elephant in the zoo drinks thirty-five litres of water a day. There are six elephants. How much water must the zookeeper make available for the elephants to drink each day? Encourage children to discuss the calculation needed in pairs and agree the method they will use, before working out the answer.

 6 x 35 litres = 210 litres.

 ***If two elephants leave, how much water would be needed now?* (140 litres)**

5 Teacher's Notes

Estimate the time it would take to walk to the dining hall from the classroom. How could you find out whether your estimate was correct or not? What equipment will you use? What unit of measure will you use?

 Use a stopwatch in seconds and minutes.

 Think of another distance in school that you think would take about the same time to walk. Try it and see.

 You may need to explain that the time taken will depend on how fast children walk or run. You could measure a distance, then test out how long it takes to cover at different speeds.

Unit 31

Name _____

1 Nazim starts on 2, Kevin starts on 3. They both double their numbers again and again. Who reaches 100 first?

2 How many odd numbers are there between 1 and 100?

3 Joshua starts on 17. Each child adds 5. Who will say 52?

Joshua   Emma   David   Beth

4 Start on 1 and count in threes. Shade the squares you land on. What do you notice?

1	2	3	4	5
6	7	8	9	10
11	12	13	14	15
16	17	18	19	20
21	22	23	24	25

5 How many crossing points are there on this grid?

Counting, properties of numbers, number sequences and reasoning about numbers

 Teacher's Notes

Nazim starts with 2 and doubles his number (2, 4, 8 and so on). Kevin starts with 3 and doubles his number (3, 6, 12 and so on). Who will say a number over 100 first?

✓ Kevin will reach 100 first because his numbers are doubling up at a faster rate than Nazim's.

➔ *Which number should you start on if you want to reach 100 in less than five steps? (7)*

2 Teacher's Notes

How many odd numbers are there between 1 and 100? Explain your answer. Children should be able to answer this without writing a list of all the numbers from 1 to 100.

✓ There are 50 odd numbers from to 1 to 100. The numbers start with 1, 2 and continue odd, even, so there are just as many even numbers as odd numbers.

➔ *How many odd numbers are there between 1 and 1000? (500)*

3 Teacher's Notes

Four children are sitting round a table. Joshua starts with the number seventeen and each child then adds on five more each time. Which child will say the number fifty-two? Encourage children to consider who cannot say 52 (Joshua and David) because of the units digits pattern 7, 2, 7, 2, ...

✓ Beth will say 52.

➔ *Will the number 86 be said? Explain your answer. (No, because counting in fives means each number said will end in 7 or 2.)*

4 Teacher's Notes

Children will need a 5 x 5 grid, showing the numbers 1 to 25. *Start on one and count on in threes colouring every number you land on. What patterns do you notice?*

✓ The numbers coloured create a pattern of diagonal lines from left to right.

➔ *Will the same pattern be created if the numbers were arranged in a four by four or a six by six grid? (The diagonal lines will go right to left on a 4 x 4 grid, and the shaded squares will form vertical lines on a 6 x 6 grid.)*

5 Teacher's Notes

Here are five lines crossed by four lines. How many crossing points are there? Encourage children to think about how they can work this out before counting each individual point.

✓ There are 20 crossing points.

➔ *Predict how many crossing points there will be if you draw five lines crossed by five lines. Draw it and count the crossing points to check your prediction.*

Unit 32

Name _____

1 One pastry weighs 50 g. Each pack holds 2 pastries. John buys 3 packs. How much do they weigh?

2 Look at these numbers. How have they been sorted?

A	B
8	3
40	15
24	30
32	21
36	6

3 How many dots in this array? Can you work out the answer without counting them all?

4 These cakes come in boxes of 4. How many boxes are needed to give a cake each to 42 people?

5 All the cars in the showroom have 4 wheels. Tom counted 54 wheels on the cars he cleaned. Is he right?

Understanding multiplication and division

UNIT 32

1 Teacher's Notes

One pastry weighs fifty grams. You can only buy pastries in packs of two. John buys three packs of pastries. How much do they weigh altogether? Encourage the children to think about what steps are needed.

✓ 300 g.

➡ ***What would be the weight of six packs of pastries?** (600 g).* **Do the children notice it is double the previous answer?**

2 Teacher's Notes

The numbers on your worksheets have been sorted according to a particular characteristic. Can you work out the characteristic that links all the A numbers together but makes them different from the B numbers?

✓ The A numbers are multiples of 4, the B numbers are multiples of 3.

➡ ***Can you create a list of C numbers who have a characteristic linking them to each other but making them different from the A numbers and the B numbers?***

3 Teacher's Notes

Here is a five by ten array. How many dots are there? How many dots are there in a five by eleven array? The children should realise that they do not need to count every dot, they just need to know how many dots in each row and column.

✓ There are 50 dots in the 5 by 10 array.

➡ ***Show in three different ways that five multiplied by ten is fifty.***

4 Teacher's Notes

A box will hold four cakes. If forty-two people each get one cake, how many boxes of cakes will be needed? Discuss whether all the cakes in the boxes will be eaten. Children should be clear that it is not possible to buy exactly 42 cakes.

✓ They will need 11 boxes. Children may say 10 boxes – ensure that they understand the importance of context.

➡ ***How many people will fifteen boxes feed if each person has one cake?** (60)*

💡 If children are confused it may help to model the problem using counters arranged in groups of 4.

5 Teacher's Notes

Every car in the showroom has four wheels and it's Tom's job to clean the wheels before the cars are sold. One day he was sure he had counted fifty-four wheels as he cleaned. Is this possible or has he miscounted?

✓ 54 is not a multiple of 4 so Tom must have miscounted.

➡ ***There were 14 cars in the showroom. How many wheels had Tom really cleaned?** (56)*

Unit 33

Name _____

1 Corinne only has 5p coins. How many does she need to buy an ice-cream for 92p?

2 Multi-packs of crisps cost £2.50 for 9 bags. You need bags of crisps for 40 children. How many multi-packs must you buy? What will they cost?

3 Adam has £46 to spend on CDs. CDs cost £5 each. How many can he buy? Will he have any money left?

4 Frank buys a ruler for 17p with 2 silver coins. What coins does he use? What change does he get?

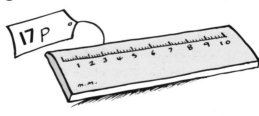

5 Amy has £2 made up of 10p and 20p coins. What coins could she have?

© T C O'Brien 2002. *Problem Solving 3.* Copying permitted for purchasing schools only. This material is not copyright free.

Money and 'real life' problems

Teacher's Notes

Corinne has only 5p coins. How many should she give to buy some ice-cream for 92p? Encourage children to think about how many 5p coins make £1 in the first instance. Some may need to use actual coins to help.

✓ She should give nineteen 5p coins.

➡ ***Using any coins, what would be the most efficient way to make exactly 92p?* (1 x 50p, 2 x 20p, 1 x 2p – 4 coins)**

Teacher's Notes

For the party next week you need to buy enough bags of crisps for every child to have one. Crisps come in multi-packs of nine bags for £2.50. There will be forty children at the party. How many multi-packs will you need to buy and how much will they cost?

✓ You will need to buy 5 multi-packs costing £12.50 (there will be some bags of crisps left over – this may confuse children).

➡ ***If individual bags of crisps can be bought for 30p, is it cheaper to buy individual bags for the party?* (Yes, it would only cost £12.00 for exactly 40 bags.)**

💡 Encourage children to discuss the steps needed to solve the problem. *What do you need to work out first?*

Teacher's Notes

Adam has £46 birthday money to spend. He wants to buy some CDs. Each CD costs £5. How many can he buy? Will he have any birthday money left over?

✓ He can buy 9 CDs and will have £1 left.

➡ ***If the price of CDs was £6, could he buy more or fewer for his money?* Ensure children understand that they can answer this question without reading the calculation. *Calculate the number of CDs priced at £6 that he could buy.* (7 CDs and £4 left)**

Teacher's Notes

Frank decided to buy a ruler which cost 17p. He didn't have the exact money and gave the shopkeeper two silver-coloured coins. The shopkeeper gave him some change. How much change did he give? Discuss which coins are silver and which two could be used to make an amount greater than 17p.

✓ He used two 10p coins, and got 3p change.

➡ ***How many other ways could 17p have been made, using any coins?***

💡 You may need to discuss why other possibilities that children suggest are inappropriate, e.g. two 20ps, 20p and 50p, etc. There would be no need for Frank to pay using these coins, as they would immediately be returned to him as change.

Teacher's Notes

Amy had £2 in total made up of 10p and 20p coins. Work out the different coin combinations she could have had. Encourage children to work systematically to find as many possibilities as they can. Some may need to use actual coins to help them.

✓ There are lots of possibilities, e.g. 10p, 10p, 10p, 10p, 10p, 10p, 20p, 20p, 20p, 20p, 20p, 20p, 20p.

➡ ***If she had three times as many 10p coins as 20p coins, which combination did she have?* (12 x 10ps and 4 x 20ps)**

Unit 34

Name _____

1 Chris had £1.40. He spent half. How much was left?

2 True or false? A multiple of 5 is always half a multiple of 10.

3 There are 20 children in the class.

$\frac{1}{2}$ have brown hair. $\frac{1}{4}$ have blonde hair.

2 have black hair. The rest have ginger hair.

How many have ginger hair?

4 Shade $\frac{1}{2}$ of rectangle A, $\frac{5}{10}$ of rectangle B, $\frac{2}{4}$ of rectangle C.

What do you notice?

   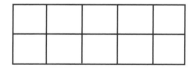   

    A   B   C

5 Estimate the fractions shaded on these shapes.

Fractions

 Teacher's Notes

On Saturday, Chris spent half of his £1.40 savings. How much was left? Remind children to convert the amount into pence first.

 70p was left.

 ***If he spends half of the remaining money on Sunday, how much would he have left?* (35p)**

 Teacher's Notes

Is this statement true or not? A multiple of five is always half a multiple of ten. Encourage children to think of some multiples of 5 then double, or multiples of 10 then halve, to see whether the statement is true.

 True, e.g. 5 is half of 10; 10 is half of 20; 15 is half of 30; 20 is half of 40…

 ***Complete this statement: a multiple of three is always half a multiple of ___* (6).**

Teacher's Notes

A class is made up of twenty children. Half of the children have brown hair; one quarter of the children have blonde hair; two children have black hair and the rest have ginger hair. Can you calculate the number with ginger hair? Encourage children to discuss what they will do first in pairs.

10 brown, 5 blonde, 2 black so 3 had ginger.

Look at the children in this class. Estimate the fraction of the class that have brown hair and the fraction that have blonde hair.

 Teacher's Notes

On your worksheets there are some rectangles labelled A, B, C.
Colour half of rectangle A red.
Colour five-tenths of rectangle B red.
Colour two quarters of rectangle C red.
What do you notice? You may need to discuss what each fraction means. e.g. colour 6 out of 10 parts, etc.

 The same amount of each rectangle has been coloured red, $\frac{1}{2} = \frac{5}{10} = \frac{2}{4}$.

 Can you draw another rectangle divided into a number of equal parts and colour an equivalent amount in red?

 Teacher's Notes

Roughly estimate the amount shaded in each of the drawings on your worksheets. Encourage the children to think about how many equal pieces the circles could be split into.

 $\frac{1}{2}$, $\frac{1}{3}$, $\frac{3}{4}$.

 Look at times shown on analogue clock faces to see when it is about half past, nearly quarter to and so on.

Unit 35

Name _____

1 I am thinking of a number. I double it and add 5.
I get 45. What is my number?

2 Write + and − signs to make this work.

4   12   40   16 = 40

3 Add 4 different numbers to make exactly 100.

4 Put a number in each box so that each row and
column add up to the same total.

2   1   2

1

3   3   3

3   2   1

5 Can you find three next-door numbers that add to 100?

Understanding addition and subtraction

  1 Teacher's Notes

I am thinking of a number. I double it and add five. I get forty-five. What was my number? Check that the children understand that they need to work backwards through the problem, i.e. subtract 5 then halve.

 The secret number is 20.

→ *Make up a 'think of a number' puzzle for your partner to solve – only have two steps to each puzzle until you get the hang of it. Explain what you need to do to solve each one.*

  2 Teacher's Notes

Look at the numbers on your worksheets. All the operation signs are missing. Use only plus and minus signs to make a calculation that is correct.

 $4 + 12 + 40 - 16 = 40$.

→ *Can you write a similar calculation using different numbers and plus and minus signs?*

 3 Teacher's Notes

Using four different numbers, add them together to make exactly one hundred. Use your calculator to help you. Try to come up with four numbers that no-one else in the class has chosen.

 There are many possible answers, for example, $26 + 22 + 23 + 29$.

→ *Use six different numbers to make exactly one hundred.*

 4 Teacher's Notes

Put one number in each box so that each row and column add up to the same total. Encourage the children to think about what the totals will be. *What are the possible totals only using these numbers?*

 Each row and column totals 6.

1	2	3
2	3	1
3	1	2

→ *Is it possible to use the digits 4, 5, and 6 in a similar way so that the total of each row and column is the same? Maybe you can use the patterns created in the previous task to help you.*

 5 Teacher's Notes

Can you find three numbers in a row (like three, four and five) that add up to one hundred? Encourage the children to think about the approximate size of the numbers, before testing any in particular.

 It is not possible. However, children should have had experience trying out different combinations of consecutive numbers perhaps realising that the numbers need to be in the 30s. 30–31–32 is too small. How about 31–3–33? Encourage them to keep going. Are children systematic? Do they try every possible series of numbers?

 → *How close to one hundred could you get?*

Unit 36

Name _____

1

Word	Tally

2 Which subject is most popular in your class? Draw a chart to show your results.

3 Find out the temperature in different countries in one month. Can you draw a graph?

4 Bluecoat School held a reading survey. Here are the results.

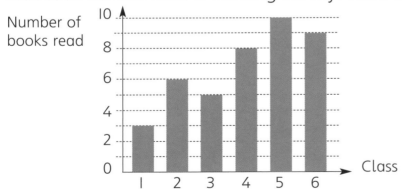

5 Do children with blonde hair usually have blue eyes? How can you find out? How will you present your results?

Handling data

Teacher's Notes

Read a passage from a book and ask children to listen. *Choose a particular word and create a tally to show the number of times I read out that word – e.g. you may have chosen 'and' or 'the' or 'boy' . . . Compare results with other children. Which of the chosen words was the most common in that passage?*

✓ This depends on the passage read and words chosen.

➔ ***Make a bar chart to show all your results visually.***

Teacher's Notes

Which subject is the most popular within your class? (maths, English, art, etc.) Create a chart to show your findings. Discuss what the children need to do, e.g. create a tally chart, work out the frequencies for each subject, draw a bar graph.

✓ This will depend on children's opinions.

➔ ***Find out whether the most popular lesson has the longest amount of time spent on it.***

Teacher's Notes

Use the internet or holiday brochures to find out the temperature in different countries during a particular month. Which country has the highest temperature? The lowest? How do they compare to the United Kingdom? Encourage children to draw a bar graph showing temperatures in different countries.

✓ This will depend which month and which countries are chosen.

➔ ***Look at one country's changing temperature during the year. Find the difference between the lowest and the highest temperature for that country.***

Teacher's Notes

Bluecoat School held a survey to see which class read the most books together in a particular week. Here are the results. Use the bar chart to answer these questions: Which class read the most books? How many more books did Class Four read compared with Class Two? How many books did Class Three read? Which class read more books than Class Three but less than Class Four?

✓ Class 5, 2 more, 5 books, Class 2.

➔ ***Write about two other facts you can see on the bar chart.***

Teacher's Notes

Do children with blonde hair usually have blue eyes? How can you gather some data to find out whether the answer to the question is yes or no? Who would you gather your information from? How would you present your information?

✓ Hopefully children will have suggested looking at the eye colour of children with blonde hair and creating some kind of tally or Carroll diagram to record this information.

➔ ***Do people who are tall generally have larger feet than people who are shorter?***

Sample medium-plan: Autumn term

Unit	Topic	Objectives; children will be taught to:	Problem Solving unit
1	Place value, ordering, estimating, rounding Reading numbers from scales	Read and write whole numbers to 1000 in figures and words. Know what each digit represents and partition three-digit numbers into a multiple of 100, a multiple of 10, and ones. Read and begin to write the vocabulary of estimation. Estimate up to 100 objects. Read scales to the nearest division.	1
2–3	Understanding + and −	Extend understanding of the operations of addition and subtraction. Read and begin to write related vocabulary. Use +, − and = signs. Recognise that addition can be done in any order.	2
	Mental calculation strategies (+ and −) Money and 'real life' problems Making decisions, checking results	Put larger number first in order to count on. Identify near doubles. Bridge through a multiple of 10 and adjust. Recognise all coins and notes. Understand £/p notation (e.g. £3.06). Find totals, give change and work out how to pay. Choose appropriate number operations and calculation methods to solve word problems. Explain and record methods informally. Check sums by adding in different order.	3
4–6	Measures, including problems	Read time to 5 minutes. Use ruler to draw and measure lines to nearest half cm. Read and begin to write the vocabulary related to length. Choose an appropriate number operation and calculation method to solve word problems. Explain and record method informally. Measure and compare using m, cm. Know relationship m, cm, km, m. Use decimal notation for m and cm. Suggest suitable units and equipment to estimate or measure lengths, including km. Read scales. Record to nearest whole/half unit, or as mixed units (e.g. 3m, 20cm).	4
	Shape and space	Classify and describe 3-D and 2-D shapes, referring to reflective symmetry, faces, sides/edges, vertices, angles.	5
	Reasoning about shapes	Read and begin to write the vocabulary of position. Use spaces on square grids. Identify right angles in 2-D shapes and in the environment. Investigate general statements about shapes.	6
7	**Assess and review**		
8	Counting, properties of numbers and number sequences Reasoning about numbers	Count larger collections by grouping them in tens, then other numbers. Count on/back in 10s/100s, starting from any two-/three -digit number. Count on or back in twos, starting from any two-digit number and recognise odd and even numbers to at least 100. Solve number puzzles. Explain methods and reasoning orally and in writing.	7
9–10	Understanding x and ÷ Mental calculation strategies (x and ÷)	Understanding multiplication as repeated addition and as an array. Read and begin to write related vocabulary. Recognise that multiplication can be done in any order. To multiply by 10/100, shift the digits one/two places to the left.	8
	Money and 'real life' problems Making decisions, checking results	Choose an appropriate number operation and calculation method to solve word problems involving money and 'real life' Explain and record method informally. Check multiplication in a different order.	9
11	Fractions	Recognise unit fractions 1/2, 1/3, 1/4, 1/5, 1/10, and use them to find fractions of shapes and numbers. Begin to recognise fractions that are several parts of a whole 2/3, 3/4, 3/10.	10
12	Understanding + and − Mental calculation strategies (+ and −) Time, including problems Making decisions, checking results	Understand that subtraction is the inverse of addition. Say a subtraction statement equivalent to an addition statement and vice versa. Find a small difference by counting up from the smaller number. Read and begin to write the vocabulary related to time. Use units of time and relationship between them. Choose appropriate number operations and calculation methods to solve word problems. Explain and record method. Check subtraction with addition.	11
13	Handling data	Solve a given problem by organising and interpreting data in frequency tables, and pictograms with the symbol representing two units.	12
14	**Assess and review**		

Sample medium-plan: Spring term

Unit	Topic	Objectives; children will be taught to:	Problem Solving unit
1	Place value, ordering, estimating, rounding Reading numbers from scales	Read and write the vocabulary of comparing and ordering numbers, including ordinal numbers to 100. Compare two three-digit numbers and say which is more or less. Read and begin to write the vocabulary of approximation. Round any two-digit number to nearest 10. Read scales and dials.	13
2–3	Understanding + and – Mental calculation strategies (+ and –)	Add three then four single-digit numbers mentally. Add three or four small numbers by putting the largest number first and/or finding pairs that total 10. Partition into 5 and a bit to add, 6, 7 or 8.	14
	Money and 'real life' problems Making decisions, checking results	Choose appropriate number operations and calculation methods to solve money or 'real life' word problems with one or more steps. Explain and record method. Check with an equivalent calculation.	15
5–6	Shape and space Reasoning about shapes	Make and describe shapes and patterns. Relate solid shapes to pictures of them. Read and begin to write vocabulary of direction. Make and use right-angled turns, and use the four compass points. Solve shape problems or puzzles. Explain reasoning and methods.	16
	Measures, and time, including problems	Read and begin to write the vocabulary related to mass. Measure and compare using kilograms and grams, and know the relationship between them. Suggest suitable units and equipment to estimate or measure mass. Read scales. Record measurements using mixed units, or to the nearest whole/half unit (e.g. 3.5 kg). Choose appropriate number operations and calculation methods to solve measurement word problems with one or more steps. Explain and record method.	17
		Read time to 5 minutes on analogue and 12-hour digit clocks (e.g. 9:40).	18
7	**Assess and review**		
8	Counting, properties of numbers and number sequences Reasoning about numbers	Count on in steps of 3 or 4 or 5 from any small number to at least 50 and back again. Create and describe simple number sequences. Investigate general statement about familiar numbers, and give examples that match them. Solve number puzzles. Explain methods and reasoning orally and in writing.	19
9–10	Understanding + and – Mental calculation strategies (+ and –)	Add three two-digit numbers using apparatus or informal methods. Partition into tens and units and recombine.	20
	Understanding x and ÷ Mental calculation strategies (x and ÷)	Understand division as grouping or sharing. Read and begin to write the related vocabulary. Recognise division is inverse of multiplication. Use doubling and halving, starting from known facts. Say or write division statement corresponding to multiplication statement.	21
	Money and 'real life' problems Making decisions, checking results	Choose appropriate number operations and calculation methods to solve money or 'real life' word problems with two steps. Explain and record method. Check results, e.g. check division by multiplication, halving by doubling.	22
11	Fractions	Begin to recognise simple equivalent fractions, e.g. 5/10 is equivalent to 1/2, 5/5 to 1 whole.	23
12	Handling data	Solve a given problem by organising and interpreting data in bar charts – intervals labelled in ones then twos.	24
13	**Assess and review**		

Sample medium-term plan: Summer term

Unit	Topic	Objectives; children will be taught to:	Problem Solving unit
1	Place value, ordering, estimating, rounding Reading numbers from scales	Compare two three-digit numbers, say which is more or less and give a number that lies between them. Round any three-digit number to the nearest 100. Order a set of whole numbers to 1000; position them on a number line. Identify unlabelled divisions on a number line or measuring scale.	25
2-3	Understanding + and − Mental calculation strategies (+ and −)	Extend understanding of addition and subtraction. Add several small numbers. Add or subtract a near multiple of 10 to a two-digit number, by adding or subtracting the nearest multiple of 10, adjusting. Use patterns of similar calculations.	26
	Money and 'real life' problems Making decisions, checking results Pencil and paper procedures	Choose appropriate number operations and calculation methods to solve money or 'real life' word problems with one or two steps. Explain and record method. Check results. Use informal pencil and paper methods to support, record or explain TU + TU, HTU ÷ TU and HTU + HTU.	27
4–6	Shape and space	Recognise that a straight line is two right angles. Compare angles with a right angle, saying whether they are more or less. Investigate general statements about shapes, and suggest examples to match them. Explore reasoning.	28
	Reasoning about shapes	Identify and sketch lines of symmetry, recognise shapes with no line of symmetry. Sketch reflection of simple shape in a mirror. Read and begin to write the vocabulary of position, direction and movement.	29
	Measures, including problems	Read and begin to write the vocabulary related to capacity. Measure and compare using litres and millilitres, and know the relationship between them. Suggest suitable units and equipment to estimate or measure capacity. Read scales. Record measurements using mixed units, or to the nearest whole/half unit (e.g. 3.5 litres). Choose appropriate number operations and calculation methods to solve measurement word problems with one or more steps. Explain and record method.	30
7	**Assess and review**		
8	Counting, properties of numbers and number sequences Reasoning about numbers	Recognise two-digit and three-digit multiples of 2, 5 and 10 and three-digit multiples of 50 and 100. Solve number puzzles. Explain methods and reasoning orally and in writing.	31
9–10	Understanding x and ÷ Mental calculation strategies (x and ÷)	Begin to find remainders after division. Round up or down after division. Use known facts and place value to multiply and divide mentally.	32
	Money and 'real life' problems Making decisions, checking results	Choose appropriate number operations and calculation methods to solve money or 'real life' word problems with one or two steps. Explain and record method. Check results.	33
11	Fractions	Compare two familiar fractions. Know that 1/2 lies between 1/4 and 3/4. Estimate a simple fraction (proportion) of a shape.	34
12	Understanding + and − Mental calculation strategies (+ and −) Pencil and paper procedures Time including problems Making decisions, checking results	Add using pencil and paper methods. Use known number facts and place value to add/subtract mentally. Use informal pencil and paper methods to support, record or explain TU − TU and HTU − TU. Use a calendar. Choose appropriate number operations and calculation methods to solve time word problems with one or two steps. Explain and record method. Check results.	35
13	Handling data	Solve a given problem by organising and interpreting data in Venn and Carroll diagrams – one criterion.	36
14	**Assess and review**		

Class Record Sheet

Class:

Name	1	2	3	4	5	6	7	8	9	10	11	12	13	14	15	16	17	18	19	20	21	22	23	24	25	26	27	28	29	30	31	32	33	34	35	36

Unit

Individual Record Sheet

Name:

Term:

Unit	Comment											